Courage, Brave Amazon
One woman's spiritual journey through breast cancer

Christine Rayner

Courage, Brave Amazon
Christine Rayner

© Copyright Christine Rayner 2002

First Published by LUCAS BOOKS 2002
www.lucasbooks.co.uk

ISBN 1903797-17-9

Cover illustration © copyright Emma Hewitt
Cover photograph by courtesy of Peter Eade

British Library Catalogue in Publication Data
A catalogue record for this book is available from the british library

Printed by Brackenbury Associates - Ipswich

For my dear husband Pete, my love, my friend and my guide.
The rock I cling to when swirling currents threaten
to drag me under.

This book is also dedicated to my Amazon Sisters the
world over, each one so brave a warrior.

Eternal Celtic Knot with the Ribbon of Remembrance
Original design © Pat Fish of Tattoo Santa Barbara, USA
Used with permission and blessing.
http://www.luckyfish.com

Contents

Foreword

At *Breast Cancer Care* we speak to thousands of women each year, just like Chrissie, who are coping with breast cancer. Each woman's experience of breast cancer is different, yet it is common to feel frightened and isolated with many unanswered questions.

In this book Chrissie explores her own feelings when faced with her diagnosis and shares her journey through breast cancer. Many people who have breast cancer find it helps to talk to someone who has faced a similar diagnosis. By sharing her story, Chrissie proves there is life after a diagnosis of breast cancer and that you can go on to have a happy, healthy and fulfilling future. This book is a testament to Chrissie's courage and determination to turn her breast cancer into a positive experience.

Breast Cancer Care is delighted to have been able to support Chrissie through her breast cancer. Donations from the sale of this book mean that Breast Cancer Care can go on helping women and men with breast cancer, their partners, family and friends for many years to come.

Stephanie Jacobs, Chair of Trustees, *Breast Cancer Care.*

Preface

I have written this book in an attempt to convey the message that even with such a devastating disease as Breast Cancer, there is hope. Treatments today are far more aggressive and effective than ever before. Nowadays, many patients make a full recovery, and have an encouraging prognosis after treatment. I sincerely hope that as you read, you may become more aware about Breast Cancer, and less frightened of knowing the facts concerning both the disease and the means by which it is treated, than perhaps you have been until now.

More often than not, it is the unknown that creates the most fear. Once we know the facts, once we are aware, we can deal with the reality instead of allowing ourselves to be frightened by our imaginings.

The book tells the story of how I dealt with my Breast Cancer after I was diagnosed in August 2000, unfailingly supported and sustained by the devoted love and care of Pete, my husband. Not only is this an account of how we lived with and fought the disease, but it is also a love story. It had to be.

My aims in writing the book are to promote awareness, and to help readers not only to gain insight into what it is actually like to be a breast cancer sufferer, or the partner of one, but also to develop an understanding of how to constructively support someone who is struggling to cope with this disease. The most effective means by which I can achieve these aims is through sharing my experiences with you. I hope my story may assist in raising your existing awareness, also that it may give you reason to believe that to have a mastectomy does not mean the loss of femininity, sexual attractiveness or self-esteem, and that whatever we lose during the course of our lives, Life itself is always worth living.

CR, May 2002

One

"I hope you can offer me some peace of mind" was the first thing I said to my consultant, as Pete and I apprehensively took our seats in his office at 10am on Friday 25th August 2000. We were there to receive the results of a biopsy that had been performed on a lump in my left breast one week previously, and we had spent the past seven days anxiously waiting for this moment. Looking me straight in the eye, my open file on his desk, the consultant replied, "I'm afraid I cannot do that". Clutching hands tightly, Pete and I were shaken to hear the words we had been dreading. I had already prepared myself psychologically and emotionally for this diagnosis, but the confirmation of it was frightening for us both. Our immediate concern was for each other. Pete held me closely and protectively as we absorbed the news that I had been diagnosed as having breast cancer.

Six months before, in February, I'd had a mammogram and ultrasound scan after discovering a lump in my breast. No abnormality was detected because no tumour was visible at that stage. The conclusion was that natural changes within the breast tissue, which occur during mid life, were causing it to feel lumpy and uncomfortable. But I kept a watchful eye on things and as time went by my breast became more painful, and the lump felt larger. I wanted another woman's opinion and asked a friend, one of the supervisors at my local gym, to see what she could feel. Her shocked reaction when she touched the lump convinced me I should ask my G.P. for a further referral to the breast consultant I had previously seen. For weeks Pete had been urging me to go and see him again, and within a couple of days I found myself in his office once more.

After I undressed, the consultant asked me to sit on the edge of the bed, facing him, and to place my hands on my head so that he could observe what there was to see. The attending nurse smiled reassuringly at me, putting me at ease. The doctor closed his eyes as he examined my breast, with an expression of intense concentration on his face, his attention fully focused on what he could feel. The examination didn't take very long and was painless.

His verdict was that the lumpy area had changed since he last saw me and an appointment was made for me to have another ultrasound scan later that week. When I went for the scan I knew what to expect, having had one back in February. I had to lie on a bed with my body turned slightly towards the examining doctor, and my arm on the affected side raised above my head. A nurse applied some gel to the area that was going to be scanned, and the sensor, which looked similar to a small torch, was connected to a monitor beside the bed. The doctor moved the sensor over the part of my breast where the lump was, then over my entire breast and armpit. The armpit area is known as the axilla and is one of the sites where lymph glands (or nodes) are to be found. Lymph is a clear fluid, supplying body cells with nutrients and disease-fighting white blood cells, as well as absorbing their waste products. The lymphatic system is one of the routes by which cancer can be spread, it being the body's transportation system. Cancer cells can migrate from the breast into the lymph glands, which is why these, or a number of them, are removed during surgery for breast cancer, and microscopically examined. It is important for women to feel their armpits as well as their breasts for lumps, when conducting their routine checks, and to see a doctor if any lump or swelling is found in that area, even if the breasts feel normal.

The doctor performing the ultrasound was polite and considerate. He continually explained what he was doing and asked me if I felt comfortable. The degree of caring made feel emotional, special, and that I mattered. That my femininity, the womanhood I have always honoured, was respected. This was very important to me.

The ultrasound scan revealed that there was an abnormality and the next step was to have a biopsy. It was at this point that I began to feel really fearful. Until then I hadn't let things worry me too much, because the scans I'd had six months earlier suggested there was nothing to worry about. Pete and I are positive thinking individuals and we had both tried to maintain the view that nothing sinister was going on. Pete had been with me every step of the way, by my side during every consultation and always going with me when I went for my scans. As he drove us to the hospital for the biopsy he told me he was confident that the result would reveal there was nothing for us to fear. But I had begun to seriously doubt that my breast was healthy. For a long time it had felt different to its partner, not as soft, stiffer, and almost unfriendly. After I'd had the first scans I'd spent a lot of time looking at its profile in the mirror. Gradually, I noticed a distinct bulge forming on its upper contour. I could feel a more thickened lumpiness just above and slightly to the left of my nipple, and when I held my arms up I noticed that the skin looked puckered. It had felt sore for several months, especially whenever Pete hugged me. Often I'd asked him not to hold me too tightly because it hurt, and Pete had reminded me of this when I was trying to decide whether to go back to my doctor or to leave it for a while longer. I tended to disregard the pain because I knew that this is sometimes a symptom accompanying the mid-life changes that had been previously diagnosed. I'd had regular routine check-ups since I began taking hormone replacement therapy in 1995, which had always reassured me that everything was satisfactory as far as my breast health was concerned. Now, going for the biopsy, I began to give serious thought to the possibility that I might have breast cancer. I hardly spoke during our drive to the hospital, trying to keep my thoughts positive.

Lying on the bed, I was told by the doctor who was to perform the biopsy that after an injection of local anaesthetic, three cores of tissue would be extracted from the suspicious area by means of a needle attached to a gun. The needle would be inserted accurately, because the exact spot could be pinpointed using the monitor beside the bed. This was reassuring, and I felt fine about the procedure being carried out. The doctor said that he would prepare me for the taking of each sample by saying the words "I'm going to fire the gun now." The anaesthetic was injected beneath my skin over the site of the lump, and stung very slightly but only for a moment or two. The biopsy itself was painless, and all I felt was a little pressure each time the gun was fired. Afterwards the nurse applied a dressing and I rejoined Pete in the waiting area. We were brought cups of tea, and I was told that my breast would feel a little sore as the anaesthetic wore off, but that if I took some standard painkillers this would help. We were told that the consultant's secretary would phone us in a few days to arrange an appointment to discuss the results of the biopsy with him. We drank our tea, left the hospital and drove home.

On the way I began to feel queasy as the anaesthetic wore off. Going over bumps in the road was uncomfortable and at times quite painful, and Pete drove as smoothly as he could for me. I went to bed when we got home but I couldn't rest. However hard I tried I could not convince myself that the biopsy result would be good. My intuition, which has served me well all my life and which I regard as one hundred percent reliable, told me to prepare myself for the worst, and during the following days I did so. I told Pete that I was anticipating bad news, and that if the result turned out to be good then this would come as a pleasant surprise. I preferred it this way. There seemed no point in trying to persuade myself that all was well. If I had taken that line, the bad news I was destined to receive would have come as a devastating blow that I would not have been able to deal with so rationally. As it later transpired, the mental preparations I made stood me in very good stead.

Back in February Pete and I had discussed how we would try to cope if cancer had been diagnosed then. At that time I'd expressed fears that if ever I had to have a mastectomy it might alter his feelings for me, that he might no longer see me as the complete woman I had always been for him. Pete was very upset by this, and had told me then that if ever I lost a breast to cancer it would make no difference to the way he felt about me or to the depth of his love for me, that he would never allow it to ruin either the things we enjoy doing together now, nor our plans for the future. There was, he said, far more between us than just flesh, and I was never to feel I might lose his love and respect should this ever happen to me. To us. We were in this together. This was how we saw it then, and how we saw it now. If the biopsy result revealed that there was anything seriously wrong with me, it went without saying that we would support each other and be there for one another as we have always been. When we married we vowed to do this. The testing time for those precious vows had come.

Two

During the following days I became very agitated. We hadn't told family or friends anything at all, preferring to wait until we knew the biopsy result. Our main concern was that our daughter Lucy should be spared any unnecessary anxiety and we didn't want to risk her being told anything about this until we knew exactly what was going on. Lucy no longer lives at home and in some respects just having each other to think about at this time of uncertainty made things a little easier for us.

I desperately wanted to know the results of the biopsy and was impatient for the phone call. When it came, my consultant's secretary told me that he wanted me to go to see him at ten o'clock the following morning. I went cold, feeling full of fear and apprehension. I expressed my anxieties to the girl who was sympathetic and very understanding. I thought that if all had been well with my result the consultant would have told me personally over the phone. Now I was convinced that the result was going to be bad for us. Professionally of course his secretary was unable to give me any more information. I thanked her and replaced the receiver, fully appreciating her position but wishing I could have been told that the biopsy showed there was nothing for us to worry about.

Immediately I phoned Pete at work. I was in a distressed state, my mind full of fears and imaginings that I felt unable to control on my own. I needed Pete. As soon as I heard his voice I felt comforted. He tried to reassure me, saying that just because the secretary did not divulge the biopsy result when she phoned, this did not automatically imply that things were bad, and whatever the result might be we could only expect to be told by the consultant himself. He said I should keep this in mind all the time, adding that he would take the following day off work to come with me, that I should try not to worry and that he would be home soon.

We spent the evening quietly together, as we usually do. Each word seemed more meaningful, each hug felt more tender and loving, than ever before. This night was very special. We have always been close and very much in love, but the loving feelings between us now were even more intense and powerful than we had ever imagined they could possibly be.

I reminded Pete that a few weeks prior to the start of our troubles I told him on waking up one morning that I had the impression of a profound change being in the air for us. I couldn't sense the nature of this change that I anticipated but I felt very aware that something would shortly occur which would dramatically alter our lives in some way. I'd said I felt we were standing at a crossroads, with a choice facing us of which path to take. This was my trusted intuition working again, and Pete remembered me saying these things to him. I asked him directly, then, what he thought the biopsy result would be. "I think it'll be all right," he said reassuringly, "please don't worry, this time tomorrow you'll feel much better and we can put the whole thing behind us." I smiled at him, loving him for his ever-present optimism. Then I asked "But what if the result isn't good?" "We'll deal with it together if that turns out to be the case, like we've always dealt with our problems. But let's not cross our bridges until we come to them." I snuggled up to him. I didn't tell him I felt we had much to worry about. Pete would know that soon enough. For now, it was more important for us to enjoy this precious evening together. With the dawning of tomorrow would come a change, perhaps the one I had foreseen, which would alter our lives forever.

Three

Inner strength is born of life's experiences. Without having difficulties and obstacles to overcome, we cannot expect to develop the depth of courage and strength of character we need to help us deal positively with whatever negative situations life throws at us. Next morning I woke feeling stronger than when I had gone to bed the night before. I knew that if the biopsy showed I did have breast cancer, the only way to handle it would be to think positively and try to take the news with as much courage as I could summon.

Pete held me closely, telling me not to be afraid and that he would be there for me whatever the biopsy result might be. When we got up we were fully focused and resolute, ready to face whatever the day would bring, good or bad, and to face it together. Throughout our marriage we have always been able to deal positively with any crisis, and we were confident that we could do so even now.

Whilst I got ready Pete walked our dog before we grabbed a quick breakfast. Our appointment with the consultant wasn't until ten o'clock but we had to leave home very early because of an extra item on our day's agenda. We'd been looking after a pet rat that needed re-homing, and I'd been put in touch with a kind woman who evidently adored rats and had agreed to take this one on. She lived about forty-five miles away, in the same direction as the consultant, and we'd worked out that if we left home at around seven thirty we could perform this errand of mercy in time to get back to see him by ten. With the rat in its cage in the back of the car we set off at seven thirty sharp. Having the animal to think about helped to take our minds off what was to come later. We arrived at the woman's house at eight forty-five and deposited the rat with her. Clearly it was going to a very good and caring home; the lady obviously loved animals and this one responded to her immediately. We often find ourselves rescuing animals and birds, and when a happy solution to a creature's plight is found it makes the effort all the more worthwhile. As we drove off, large butterflies began to swirl around in my stomach. Now we were embarking on the real business of the day. That extra journey had merely provided a welcome distraction. Our new priority was to arrive promptly for our appointment.

As Pete drove, I sat in silence for most of the time. No matter how desperately I tried, I could not rid myself of the idea that within the hour I would be told I had breast cancer. I felt surprisingly calm and in control, and I hoped I could maintain this composure, as much for Pete as for myself. I didn't want him to feel afraid for me, and the thought of his reaction to the diagnosis I anticipated broke my heart. I couldn't bear to contemplate it. When you love someone deeply it is inevitable that his or her pain becomes yours. Love always demands its price. But how immeasurable are the rewards, worth every sacrifice we make, every tear we shed with and for that one, special person with whom we have chosen to share our life. Preoccupied with these thoughts I became so absorbed in them that I was suddenly surprised to find we had reached our destination. The time was ten minutes to ten. Punctuality is something we both prioritise and it was a relief to know we were on time.

As we got out of the car my consultant was striding across the car park towards the rear entrance of the consulting rooms. Glancing across in our direction he uttered a non-committal "Good morning" and continued on into the building. I suddenly felt very nervous. Pete gave my hand a squeeze as we walked the short distance to the main entrance. We both agreed that positive thinking was what we needed now, as we prepared to face the greatest challenge we have ever known. Which returns us to the point at which this story began . . .

Four

I clung to Pete as the consultant's words echoed and throbbed in my head, stunned to hear him say he was unable to give me the peace of mind I had hoped for. Instead, I had received the answer I'd been expecting and fearing. I was thankful that I'd had the strength to prepare myself for it, because although this in no way softened the blow, it undoubtedly helped us both to deal with what was nonetheless a terrible shock. "It's all right, my love" Pete said gently, "let's listen to what the doctor has to say." My eyes filled with tears at that point and, as always, Pete delved into his trouser pocket and passed me his handkerchief. It's a long-established fact that I never seem to have one on me and always have to borrow his. I felt comforted by it as I wiped away the tears. I looked at Pete's face. His eyes were fixed intently on the consultant's as he waited for the full explanation of the diagnosis, his fingers tightly clasped around my hand. I felt protected and safe with Pete beside me as I asked "Is it malignant, then?" "Yes, I'm afraid it is" came the reply, "but the good news is it isn't as serious as it might be." We listened attentively as the consultant went on to explain his findings.

He told us that my cancer was of the lobular type, situated in the lobes of the breast tissue, but he went on to add that he felt it was unlikely to have spread into the lymph glands at this stage. He said that lobular breast cancer tends to be oestrogen receptor positive, (which means it is attracted to oestrogen within the oestrogen receptors in the breast, oestrogen being one of the female sex hormones), that it is less common and more difficult to find than many of the more usual forms of breast cancer but, once discovered, it is the most straightforward type to deal with. As the consultant explained it all to us we both began to feel hopeful and slightly less fearful. The more we listened to what he had to say, the more reassured we became.

What really did concern me at this stage was why the cancer hadn't been discovered when I had the mammogram and ultrasound scan six months before. The consultant explained that lobular breast cancer can be extremely difficult to detect by either method until it reaches a certain stage and size. Breast tissue is so dense that it can make identification of these types of tumours very difficult. The lumpy area I had felt at that time was due to changes taking place in the tissues surrounding the site in which the tumour was developing. The important thing was that it had been identified now, and was in all probability curable.

Turning then to the subject of treatment, he told us there were two options. Firstly, he would be able to remove just the lump. As he spoke I looked at Pete, whose doubtful expression told me he was thinking along the same lines as I was. The consultant went on; "But because of the very nature of these lobular tumours . . ." and here I interrupted him. "A mastectomy?" I asked. He replied that this was the preferable option, given that lobular breast cancer tends to be multi-focal and is known to proliferate throughout the breast tissue to the extent that tumours can be present in number. I could easily have others; the biopsy indicated that some cells were already showing signs of being likely to develop into malignancies in the future. A mastectomy to remove the whole breast would undoubtedly be the most sensible course of action, but the choice was mine. My mind, and our minds, had already been made up. We gave no thought whatsoever to the first option of having a lumpectomy. It made far more sense to be rid of the entire breast and hopefully the entire problem; we had no doubt about this. The consultant's view was that a mastectomy would act as a kind of 'insurance policy' for the future, which would give us peace of mind, knowing that the cancer had been eradicated. A future was what we wanted more than anything. Nothing else mattered.

Then the consultant told me that I could have reconstructive surgery if I wished, either during the operation to remove my breast or at some future date. He explained that in cases where breast reconstruction was performed during a mastectomy operation, he worked alongside a skilled plastic surgeon whose expertise would be likely to produce an excellent result. But as with all operations there are risks. Reconstruction can be a lengthy procedure involving many hours of anaesthesia. There may also be problems afterwards with infection and rejection, which can present serious difficulties. I wasn't at all interested in it at that time because I felt I had enough to handle in getting the cancer dealt with, and Pete agreed with me. I explained to the consultant that I believed I would be able to accept the loss of my breast, and that I wanted nothing more than a healthy, wholesome body. He respected my view although went on to say I could opt for breast reconstruction at any time in the future if I so wished. But because I stressed that this was something I didn't want to have to think about at the present time, we moved swiftly on to discussing the details of the mastectomy operation itself.

The first thing I wanted to know was whether my nipple would be removed. I had no idea, at that stage, what such an operation entailed. During a mastectomy the entire breast is removed, leaving nothing but a scar where it once was. I asked about the size of the scar and where exactly on my chest it would be. The consultant understood my need to have these questions answered, telling me that the scar would extend from the centre of my chest to beneath my armpit. He explained that during the operation he would remove some of the lymph glands from my armpit, so that they could be examined to see if any cancer cells had spread that far. The possibility that this might have happened really alarmed me, although the consultant told us that due to what the results of the tests on my cancer had already told him, he expected to find my lymph glands clear. I trusted him, knowing he wouldn't say such a thing unless he was fairly certain that it would be so.

He said we had time to fully consider what we wanted to do but that he wouldn't be happy to leave things any longer than three weeks. He clearly approved when we asked him to arrange the mastectomy as soon as he could. For us to have been able to make this decision quickly and relatively easily was the direct result of the mental preparations I had already made during the past week, coupled with Pete's support and full understanding of the situation we possibly might find ourselves in one day if we didn't act upon the advice we were given now. At this point the conversation lightened, our tension eased, and the consultant's secretary brought us all a cup of coffee. He told us that ideally he hoped to arrange for the operation to take place in a week's time. It was then that I fully appreciated the seriousness of the situation. The mastectomy would probably save my life.

After the coffee I needed the toilet and as I made my way to the bathroom I thought it might be beneficial for Pete to have a few moments alone with our consultant. For him to be able to talk 'man to man' with this doctor was, I felt, a good idea. Entering the small room I glanced down into the bath, where there crouched a very large spider. It didn't move at all whilst I answered the call of Nature and washed my hands. I admit to not being very keen on spiders but I felt a genuine liking for this one; spiders are traditionally lucky and I regarded it as a good omen. I thanked it for being there as I closed the door. Returning to the consulting room I was relieved to find Pete and the doctor smiling and chatting together, Pete looking much more relaxed. I was glad I'd left him alone with the doctor for that brief spell, knowing it would have given him the opportunity to voice any fears or concerns he might not have felt comfortable about mentioning when I was in the room.

As I sat down, the consultant said there was one more detail to discuss, which was his need to see me again before the operation to introduce me to his breast care nurse. She would be responsible for the support and advice I would need after the surgery, regarding special exercises I would have to do, the fitting of a prosthesis and so on, and any remaining questions we might have could be answered before the operation took place. The consultant said he would like to arrange the appointment for next Tuesday and that he would phone us later in the day to confirm this.

As we prepared to leave, he shook hands with us warmly, reassuring us that he held no doubts that my cancer could and would be cured. I knew our future lay in his hands. We had indeed reached that crossroads of my vision, and had chosen our path. It was signposted 'HOPE'.

Five

As Pete drove us home the tears poured down his face. Throughout the consultation he had been very strong and controlled, intent on hearing the exact details of the nature of my cancer, asking all the relevant questions regarding how it would be treated and about the prognosis we could expect. His concern throughout was solely for me, as were now his tears. "You don't deserve this," he said, choking on them. "Who does?" I replied. He put on his sunglasses. I hated seeing Pete so upset. I shed tears myself then, but only a few, at that stage. I still felt frightened but somehow I managed to remain strong and calm as well, and kept a grip on myself. Because the consultant's attitude had been so positive I considered we had good reason to be optimistic, but I fully understood Pete's reaction and knew how much those tears needed to flow.

We talked about the crisis we now faced throughout the journey home, agreeing that although we knew we had a lot to go through, we would never allow this thing to beat us. Pete confessed that he had never really felt confident about the biopsy result, but he hadn't wanted me to be aware of this until now. He'd been determined to stay cheerful and positive during all those days of waiting in order to help me keep my spirits up. But I had realised this, knowing he was putting on a brave face for my sake, just as I'd been doing for his. We had both known what had really been going on each other's minds during the past week, but we'd kept this to ourselves. We agreed that from now on we would talk to one another about everything, keeping nothing back, and that we would share all the concerns, doubts and fears we knew we would be sure to experience during the difficult days that lay ahead of us. We realised how important it would be for us to talk frankly and openly about our worries, and that we should withhold nothing. We knew it would be vital for each of us to feel comfortable about confiding even our most sinister and disturbing fears to one another, and we were glad of our long-standing ability to discuss things candidly, which has served us well over the years, and which we knew would help us now.

We decided to spend the remainder of the day together in the security, privacy and quiet calm of our home. From the moment we'd been told I had breast cancer neither of us had wanted to leave the other's side. What we needed now was to be alone together, not only to console and comfort each other but also to be able to talk things through thoroughly and formulate some kind of coping strategy, a united front of tenacity and optimism with which we could journey into the, as yet, unknown. We felt as if we were preparing to go into battle, warriors with a formidable enemy to defeat. We intended to emerge from the fight victorious. Our campaign had already begun.

Arriving home, I thought how different our lives seemed now. In the space of a few hours everything had changed. Things were not the same as they'd been when we left the house that morning, and I felt unfamiliarly insecure as I unlocked the front door. It was a glorious late summer day, very warm with hardly a cloud in the sky. Pete suggested we had a cup of coffee in the garden. We spend a considerable amount of time doing just that and today it was important for us to maintain a sense of normality, as far as we could. Routine seemed to offer comfort, providing a kind of lifeline for us to cling to. Pete switched on the kettle, and just as we'd collapsed into each other's arms there came a knock on the front door.

I answered it to find a woman I knew standing there, obviously feeling uncomfortable about disturbing us although of course she had no idea what was going on. I sensed at once that she had a problem. A bird was trapped in her greenhouse and she had come to ask if I would go and rescue it. Turning to Pete, I said I wouldn't be long. He gave me a knowing smile. He is used to people coming to find me when animals or birds are in trouble, and it was ironic that on this of all days someone needed my help, at a time when all I really wanted to do was stay in my own home with Pete's arms around me. If this poor lady had only known what we were going through! I had no intention of telling her we were having a bad time at that moment because I didn't want to embarrass her, and besides, I was happy to go help her free the bird. Together we walked the short distance to her house. The young collared dove was stressed and too frightened to find its way out of the greenhouse door. I caught it fairly easily, although the man of the house hadn't been too happy when I'd asked him to empty his greenhouse of all the plant pots and seed trays behind which the poor thing had been attempting to conceal itself! I put the bird into a cardboard box and left it in a quiet, dark place in the couple's house to recover from its ordeal. The woman told me she would be able to release it herself later on, thanked me for helping her out, and I left. To me it seemed strange that even then, when my life had been turned upside down, a small creature in distress needed my help. The thought gave me strength and made me feel a little braver, for it occurred to me that if my purpose was to be around for animals and people in need, then maybe I was destined to be cured of my cancer so that I could carry on helping them. To my way of thinking, the incident had been a sign, and I felt surprisingly light-hearted as I walked back to our house, glad of the episode, for not only had it helped to distract my mind from the bad news I'd received earlier, but it had also given me the notion that I was meant to survive, and would do so.

Six

Pete had been looking out for me returning from the bird rescue, and as I walked in the door the welcoming aroma of the coffee he had ready and waiting was comforting. Together we went out into the garden. It was very quiet as we sat down on our bench beneath the cherry tree, at the perimeter of a circle of stones. This part of our small garden is a tranquil and peaceful sanctuary, a perfect place in which to just sit and think quiet thoughts. Most of the stones are local flints, but the four cardinal points are marked by different types of stone that we have brought home from our travels around the country. Sitting there beside Pete I glanced across at the taller monolith marking North, recalling how he'd struggled to carry it to the car after managing to extricate it from its bed in a rugged hillside on the moors, somewhere near the highest point in Yorkshire. Being aware that I was at that time on the lookout for a special stone to mark the position of North, Pete knew this was the one, and he'd presented it to me with great satisfaction, knowing how delighted I would be with it.

Gazing steadily at this stone I focused my thoughts on the qualities associated with the northern element of Earth; solidity, stability, strength, steadfastness, foundation, endurance, all virtues that I knew I would need to reinforce within myself in order to get through what lay ahead of me. Sitting there beneath the tree, Pete by my side, surrounded by lovely plants, the still air full of birdsong, I knew clearly who I was, where I had come from and more importantly, where I was going.

Spending time together beside our stone circle was something that was necessary for us to do, to help ourselves adjust psychologically and spiritually to the new situation we were in. Sometimes we spoke, mostly we just held hands and were silent. A feeling of disbelief had infused my whole being, a sensation that this was merely a dream, far removed from reality. Pete said he felt the same way. It was extraordinary.

Everything felt strange instead of familiar. Nothing felt like it used to. Something had intruded into our lives, like an unwelcome visitor to whom we could not wait to show the door. We were determined to slam the door in this one's face so hard that it would jam shut and remain closed forever. Visualising this concept, I felt my strength energising, my inspiration flowing. I knew my courage would nourish Pete's, my strength would become his strength and his mine. This is how it worked for us. This is how it was, is, and will ever be. We spent several hours sitting quietly together in the peace of the garden, and gradually we began to accept what had happened. All that was left for us to do that day was to decide how to break the news to family and friends. We knew it would be difficult for everybody, but we agreed that the sooner we told everyone, the less burdensome the prospect would be for us. The only real problem lay in knowing with whom to start, and as we were discussing this we were interrupted by the sound of the phone ringing. I ran indoors followed closely by Pete. It was the consultant. He asked me how I was feeling, and when I replied that I felt fine he sounded pleasantly surprised, saying "Well done, that's very good." Tuesday was confirmed as the date for the pre-op chat and he suggested we brought a list of any further questions we needed to ask him. Our brief conversation was warm and friendly. I told the consultant I would look forward to seeing him on Tuesday and we left it at that. Now it was time for us to face the daunting task of telling the family.

Seven

From the moment we were told I had breast cancer I was determined that our family and friends should be positive. I had no time for negative reactions and didn't want them. Neither did I want an overload of sympathy. I needed people to be strong and optimistic for us. Cancer is a small word but those six letters hold a great deal of power, conjuring up immediate fear in anyone who is diagnosed, and their loved ones. This is understandable, given that the disease, of which there are so many different forms, is a life-threatening one. I desperately wanted to get the message across that the situation Pete and I were in was not a hopeless one. I knew that on hearing the word 'cancer' those close to us would initially react by feeling shock, dread and fear, and I hoped everyone in our lives would try to focus on the consultant's positive attitude and his view that a good prognosis could be expected, providing I had the mastectomy. It was, after all, what Pete and I trusted and believed in.

As far as Pete's family was concerned we decided to ask his sister to break the news to their parents, and we phoned to ask her to come to see us. Although visibly shaken at first, she took it fairly well, responding positively, which we liked. I wished that I could have spoken to my own sister face to face, but as she lives abroad this wasn't possible, and I phoned her. Liz was distraught when I told her what had happened, very upset and worried. I knew that she wasn't going to be as easily convinced that my prognosis was good, and I had to work hard to encourage her to believe that all would be well. Liz is almost fifteen years my junior, and we didn't grow up together like most siblings do. But despite this we have always been close in our adult lives, and recent years have seen this closeness blossom and grow into the strong, sisterly bond that exists between us now. I believe we humans become better equipped to deal with disturbing news as we age, because we have seen more of life, both good and bad. Liz, not having had first-hand experience of cancer in a close relative, was understandably terrified for me. But we ended our conversation on a positive note, and she made me promise to keep her up to date with developments as and when they occurred. I knew how valuable her support would be, and also how important it was for her to be kept informed about what was happening.

Liz is dependable, reliable and loyal. The regular contact she maintained with us, both before and after my operation and throughout my subsequent treatment with chemotherapy and radiotherapy, was comforting and a tremendous morale-booster. She wanted to be involved, to be there for us. I felt very close to Liz as we talked, as if she was standing right there beside me. As I replaced the receiver I felt a warm, glowing sensation filling my heart and soul. My love for my sister so overwhelmed me at that point that I burst into tears, wishing I could hold and comfort her and tell her I was going to be all right. Love can bestow upon us the curse of agonising pain as well as the blessing of infinite joy. As Pete and I, exhausted, prepared for an early night, the words of a Lebanese poet, whose beautiful writings have inspired me throughout my life, chased around in my brain: *"For even as Love crowns you, so shall he crucify you."**

*From 'The Prophet', written in 1923 by Kahlil Gibran (1883-1931)

Eight

That night in bed I sobbed uncontrollably. Pete held me in his arms, crying with me.

After a while, my tears subsided and I lay quietly with my head on his chest. There was no need for words. Each of us knew how the other was feeling, and the thoughts that were in one another's minds. All I wanted was my life, to be there for Pete for a long time yet, and to grow old with him. Often we have discussed what we think we'll do when the inevitable happens and the time comes for us to be parted. I have always told Pete that I love him too much to bear either the thought of losing him, or the thought of him losing me and being alone, without me. It would be a no-win situation. All these things were in our minds this night, but we kept reminding each other about the consultant's positive outlook on my case, comforting ourselves with the fact that he had said my cancer was curable, and believing in this. This, and our love for one another, was all we had to believe in.

At last we fell asleep, but I woke in the early hours of the next morning in a state of panic and fear. I called out to Pete. "What is it, my darling?" he whispered, reaching for me. I really let go then, and broke down completely. I desperately needed to tell him I loved him. "I love you I love you I love you" I whimpered, over and over again, without a pause and scarcely a breath between the words. I couldn't stop myself and they just tumbled out. I repeated them so many times that eventually I couldn't speak aloud and was only able to whisper. Choking sobs made my speech incomprehensible. Pete understood that I needed to release all this emotion, and tried to calm me by telling me he loved me too, all the time, but I couldn't stop and just went on and on until I was thoroughly spent. For as long as we've been together, few days have passed when we haven't spoken those three important little words to one another, but tonight they absolutely overflowed from me in a cascade of consuming emotion and torrential tears. At last, thoroughly drained, I fell asleep. I was content, knowing I'd told my dear man how much he meant to me, that he was in no doubt as to the depth of my feelings for him, and that if anything should happen to me he would always remember this night and be in no doubt as to how very much I loved him. Now, I knew I could cope with anything. With Pete beside me, I would be strong enough to face all the challenges that having breast cancer would inevitably present me with, and to face them with perseverance, courage, determination and dignity.

Nine

Waking up on Saturday 26th August I felt very odd. Emotionally speaking it was a mixed bag; although still feeling fear and disbelief after yesterday's unfolding of events, I found I was able to accept the reality more easily after a night's sleep. I felt both apprehensive about and strangely energised by the prospect of telling our friends that I had breast cancer, which was bizarre. Apprehensive because I had no idea as to how they would react, energised because I considered this to be the greatest challenge I had ever faced in my life, and although the thought that I had breast cancer wasn't something I was enjoying having, in a way I looked forward to proving to myself how strong I could be. This way of thinking motivated and empowered me. It was the only way for me, I didn't want to be molly-coddled by anyone, nor did I intend to wallow in self-pity, or use my having cancer as a means of getting attention or making people feel sorry for me. That would only have been counter-productive, taking away my ability to use my own strength to help me deal with what I had to face, and making me become too dependent on other people. I realised how difficult it would be for our friends to not feel fearful for me, but was determined they would listen to all we had to tell them, in hopes that they too would become charged with our confidence and positive outlook. Pete felt the same way. This was our mutual resolution.

I couldn't wait to get out and begin telling people our news. I knew how important it would be for us to have our friends' good thoughts with us both before and after my operation, and felt no embarrassment at the prospect of them knowing that I had breast cancer and was going to have my breast removed. It was a fact. We all have bodies and I saw no need to hide what was happening to mine.

It was at this point that the Amazon concept entered my head. Its presence in my mind grew so strong that I couldn't rid myself of it. The Amazons were a mythical nation of female warriors, trained for war and hunting. They were so-named (translated from the Greek the word means 'without breasts') because their habit was to cut off a breast in order to facilitate the throwing of spears and the drawing of their bows. Throughout history the term 'Amazon' has been used in relation to warrior women. Lying there in bed, I pictured myself as an Amazon. A female warrior, ready for a fight, and ready to win it. The more I visualised this, the stronger I felt myself becoming. It was wondrous! I told Pete about this vision, and he said it was a good one, appropriate for me because for years I have cherished the desire to learn how to shoot a longbow. It's just one of those things I've always wanted to do. I was pleased that the Amazon concept suited me. Pete said he could already see that it was filling me with energy and enthusiasm. We both liked it, and from here on, I *was* Amazon!

We had our weekend shopping to do, and as we walked to the town centre I was determined that we'd spread the positive message that although I had breast cancer I wasn't under a death sentence. I knew I was going to be all right and I needed to know everyone believed this. I felt a compulsion to tell everybody we saw. It was very strange and I have never experienced anything like it before. Pete seemed to understand and was prepared for the morning's shopping expedition to be a long one.

Reaching the lane that leads into the main street my heart gave a lurch, my mouth went dry and I began to shake. The anticipation was almost unbearable, and the adrenalin was really flowing. I glanced quickly up and down the crowded street. The town was overflowing with visitors, many of whom had come for the August Bank Holiday. I thought it would be difficult to spot our friends among so many strangers. But I couldn't have been more wrong. Halfway up the street and heading in our direction, was Ray. I tugged Pete along in my desperation to reach this friend, whom I have known since my early teens and who was one of a number of 'special people' I really hoped to see that morning. I couldn't get to him quickly enough.

Ray has always made me feel he respects both my spiritual beliefs and my philosophy of life. We spend quite a lot of time discussing such things, often in the middle of this bustling street, always oblivious to the activity around us because of the depth in which we tend to become engrossed in conversation. Ray's reaction to my news completely threw me. He was devastated, and his eyes filled with tears. His words "Oh no, not you Chrissie" shook me, and I realised just how sensitively I would need to talk to those who really are good, solid, loyal and loving friends. I also knew I was right in wanting to tell as many of them as I could as soon as possible, to be sure that they wouldn't hear about me from anyone else. As news spreads swiftly around a small community the facts often become distorted, and I wanted everyone to hear the truth about my cancer, and the good prognosis we had been told to expect, and to hear this from us.

I told Ray about the consultant's view that my breast cancer was curable, saying I wanted him to believe this. Then I mentioned the Amazon connection, knowing he would understand its relevance to my situation. He was clearly impressed by this, and I was happy to see the sparkle return to his eyes. After the three of us had spent half an hour talking together, Ray looked as if he was feeling much easier. We assured him we would keep him informed, and as he walked away from us I felt very moved by his fear and concern for me. It touched me deeply to witness that degree of caring in someone whose connection to us is solely through friendship. Pete and I both marvelled at it. As we were to later marvel at the amount of genuine concern and care shown to us by all the friends and acquaintances we told, both on that day and during the days leading up to my mastectomy. It was phenomenal. By the time we got home, laden with our shopping, we were exhausted. We had seen every one of the half dozen special folk on my mental list, plus many others. All had been told the same story, some to a greater degree than others. The main thing was that folk had heard it as it was, as we knew it to be.

Ours is a closely-knit community of people who, when members of that community are in trouble, care a great deal and show it. Pete and I were both hoarse after so much talking. But it had been a satisfying morning, and well spent. The more folk we told, the more at ease we felt with the situation. The constructive reactions from positive people were wonderful, and strengthened us. But because cancer is such a serious disease, we understood when some openly reacted with alarm and even horror. Happily, most people we told were visibly infected with our positivity. It radiated from us, shining like a beacon in the dark. For us to have been able to convey our news to others in such a way that they, too, believed my breast cancer was curable was a great blessing. The few who reacted negatively upset and irritated me. Although I felt I'd been able to reassure most people that I was going to be all right, I detected an aura of gloom and despondency around some. I was determined to prove these wrong, to show them that I wasn't going to be beaten by breast cancer whatever they thought, although of course I understood that their anxieties stemmed from the fear the word generates. But I got this into perspective, separating the depressing reactions of the minority from the reality of my awareness that I'd been told I had a reasonably good prognosis. This knowledge was like a kind of raft, keeping us afloat as we tossed and rolled upon the rough swell of an ocean of uncertainty. We clung to it like rats clinging to a sinking ship's timbers. We knew that eventually we would come to dry land if we held on to it, and to each other, tightly enough. Neither of us was prepared to let go, however deep the water or how rough the ride. After this morning we knew we were not alone, out on that tumultuous sea. Others were there with us, throwing ropes and lines for us to grasp, shining their lanterns on the waters to guide us home. We knew we would make it to the shore, with their help and our determination to ride out the storm. Our raft would take a battering, but with so many little ships around us we couldn't fail to make it to harbour safely. With their support, encouragement and guidance there would be no need for the lifeboat to be launched.

Ten

We spent the remainder of that weekend at home, venturing out only to take the dog for a walk. Pete didn't want to leave my side, and decided to ask for some leave from work. He had been very moved by folk's reactions to the news that I had breast cancer and, what with that plus the stress of having to handle the shock, he was thoroughly drained and mentally exhausted. We both were. In the space of a couple of days we had dealt with hearing the consultant's verdict, coped with the prospect of me having a mastectomy, come to terms with both concepts and the implications, and told family and friends about it all. We needed to be quiet and alone at home now for a while. Pete and I have always been an independent couple, never ones to burden other people with our problems, always sorting things out by ourselves whenever possible. We are proud of this, and were determined that even now we would survive as best we could without imposing on anyone or worrying them with our concerns and fears, because we knew this would add to our mutual strength and our ability to cope with our crisis together. I longed for the coming days to pass quickly so that this calamity could be all over and done with and we could resume our normal life.

The following Monday was a bank holiday. On the green the usual fair was being held to raise money for a local charity. We went to have a look at what was going on, and I felt relaxed as I walked around. Everything seemed almost normal, and at times it was as if I'd dreamed the whole thing, until reality intruded, invading my peace with its vivid, stabbing flashbacks of the events of Friday. I tried to disregard them. But they were never very far away.

The little stalls were full of fascinating things but I wasn't interested in buying anything. I was happy just to wander and browse. I thought Pete might need to chat to a few people by himself, so I suggested we split up for a while. I was glad when we rejoined each other, because I'd felt insecure without him beside me. We walked home in the sunshine, feeling refreshed after the break from the house but looking forward to getting out in the garden on our own.

We had an important issue to discuss and a decision to be made, which had to be made today. Our daughter Lucy still had to be told about my breast cancer. She is our only child, and in two days' time it was her twenty-first birthday. She and her partner Neal were due to arrive next day after returning from a short holiday. Because she was away on the day we received the bad news, Lucy knew nothing about it, and I didn't want to phone and ruin their holiday. This presented us with a terrible dilemma. When we next saw her it would be the eve of her birthday. However were we going to be able to tell our daughter, at such a special time in her life, that I had breast cancer? There was no way round it. Just contemplating the thought felt catastrophic, as though something precious was about to be destroyed. Lucy had emphatically stated that she didn't want a party, preferring to spend her birthday quietly with us, going out for a meal together the night before and enjoying the informal visits from family and friends who would pop in to see her on the day. I told Pete I wanted nothing to change, that we'd celebrate with Lucy and Neal just as we'd planned. He agreed, but made the valid point that we needed to decide exactly when to tell them. We knew it would be far from easy. It was difficult enough for us to have to tell Lucy I had breast cancer, but to have to do it when she was about to celebrate what should be the happiest, most memorable birthday of her life was agonising and heartbreaking. The thought of it devastated me. We had all been looking forward to Lucy's twenty-first, and she was so excited about it. Now, something had happened which could potentially ruin this precious and significant occasion for us all. But we knew it would only do so if we let it, and in no way did I intend to allow my breast cancer to turn my daughter's twenty-first birthday celebration into a tragedy. I was determined that somehow we would think of a solution to the problem, certain that between us we could break the news to Lucy in such a way that, after the initial shock was over, she would find the courage to accept what was happening, and to deal with it in her own way. She had Neal to support her and we both realised how important his role would be in this. We felt for them both as we sat down together to discuss how we should tell them.

Eleven

We sat under the tree in the garden, to talk over our problem. Regarding when to tell Lucy the news, we had several options. We could tell her as soon as she and Neal got here. Or we could leave it until later, before we all went out to dinner. I thought Lucy wouldn't want to go if we chose this option, so what was the alternative? Should we tell her after we came home? Even worse, should we leave it until the next day, which was her birthday? The problem seemed insurmountable. A lot of people had asked us how Lucy had reacted to the news that I had breast cancer. When we told them that as yet she knew nothing about it, and that the only opportunity we had to tell her was on or just before her twenty-first birthday, everyone said they felt very sorry for all of us. It just seemed as though something had orchestrated events in such a way as to make things as difficult as possible for us. Having to tell Lucy about my breast cancer at this time seemed so unfair, too cruel and unreasonable for words. To us it felt as though reason wasn't even part of the equation. We didn't know what to do. To complicate matters, tomorrow was the day on which I had to see the consultant for the pre-op. discussion. Lucy and Neal weren't due to arrive until the afternoon. By then we would be back from our appointment, which was in the morning. The day, therefore, looked like being a hectic one. I knew Lucy would be on my mind all the time whilst I was trying to concentrate on what the consultant had to say. But it was no use allowing this to upset me and I was confident that somehow I would be able to manage. I had to, and that was all there was to it.

A couple of days after Lucy's birthday she and Neal were going off to Hampshire. Neal was taking her to meet his family for the first time. They were leaving on Friday, the day of my operation. I knew that when we told Lucy about me she wouldn't want to go. I wanted her to, and felt thoroughly sickened by the prospect of having to tell her something that would spoil yet another event in her life which should be happy and enjoyable. It all felt as though we were under some kind of curse, or evil spell. Whatever we did, however we did it, nothing could alter the fact that Lucy's birthday and her meeting Neal's family would be overshadowed by what had happened to me. I could hardly bear the pain of it.

After talking all the options through, we decided it would be best if Pete told Neal the news first, after we returned from our evening out together. Neal, probably knowing Lucy better than we did now, might be able to suggest when the best time for us to tell her would be. This seemed a sensible idea, although we realised it meant we would have to be very strong and guarded throughout the afternoon and evening until Pete had an opportunity to talk to Neal. We knew this would be easier said than done but we decided to give it a go. I didn't envy Pete, with whom the ultimate responsibility for breaking our bad news to them rested.

That evening I decorated Lucy's birthday cake, which had been made and iced in plain white by our local baker. As I did so I remembered all the birthday cakes I'd created for her since she was a baby. With the exception of this and her eighteenth I had made every one, decorating them in all kinds of imaginative designs over the years. This one was the most special of all, and as I wrote "Happy 21st Lucy" I could feel the tears pricking my eyes. In the centre I placed the celtic serpent bracelet I had bought for her, a special gift because it was identical to the one I wear which Lucy has always admired. It looked pretty good as a cake decoration!

As I tidied up and put the cake away in a secret place, I felt distraught. I was heartbroken. So much was happening that I could hardly cope with it all. But I was entitled to feel sad. Lucy had reached the age of maturity and this was probably the last birthday cake I would ever decorate for her. Any mother would understand that this thought alone was enough to prompt a few tears. As for the rest of it, nobody could begin to understand how I was feeling. For twenty-one years the vision of this most important birthday had rested serenely in the back of my mind. Never once, in all that time, had I imagined that anything but joy would bless this occasion. If anyone had said that I'd be telling Lucy I had breast cancer on her twenty-first, I'd have laughed in that person's face. Now, I felt Fate was laughing at me. It all seemed so undeserved. But, as with every crisis in life, we have to face the trial head-on, and endure it as best we can. I knew for certain that instead of being happy and carefree, the next couple of days would prove to be some of the most traumatic and testing Pete and I had ever known.

Lying in bed that night my thoughts turned reluctantly to the arranged meeting with my consultant next morning. I wished I didn't have to go, knowing I'd need all my inner strength to put on a brave face for Lucy in the afternoon. I prayed for wisdom and guidance as I closed my eyes, surrendering myself to the welcome peace and refuge of sleep.

Twelve

The consultant welcomed us with a broad smile and a cheery "Good morning" as he showed us into his office. He introduced us to his breast care nurse, and I welcomed her presence. It was reassuring for me to have another woman in the room, someone who possibly understood even more than Pete and the consultant what the prospect of losing my breast meant to me.

As we sat down the doctor continued. "Everything is organised for Friday," he said, asking if we'd brought our list of further questions. When we told him that we hadn't felt it necessary to make a list he looked surprised. I said I just wanted to get on with having the operation, and that he had answered most of our questions during last Friday's consultation. Everything was clear in our minds, we felt fully informed and ready to proceed.

The consultant went straight on to explain that this nurse and one other were part of his team, which consisted of many professionals, each playing a vital role in looking after his patients. The two breast care nurses were responsible for providing aftercare, giving information and instructions about the exercises I would need to do after the surgery, diet and nutrition, literature on mastectomy bras, and the fitting of my prosthesis (breast form). He touched briefly on the subject of breast reconstruction again, saying that if I ever changed my mind about this it would be possible for me to have it done a year after the operation. I still had no interest at all in having reconstructive surgery. Instead, I was more concerned with knowing about the technicalities of the operation; how long it would take, how the wound would be stitched, what kind of dressing would be applied, how soon it would be removed, and so on. These were the things I really wanted to talk about, and I hadn't given much thought to them until now.

The consultant outlined the procedure that would be carried out on the day of the operation. We were to arrive at the hospital at seven forty-five on Friday morning. A nurse would show me my room and help to prepare me for the operation, which was to take place around eleven am. Prior to the surgery I'd receive a routine visit from the anaesthetist. The length of time the mastectomy would take to perform was roughly one to one and a half hours. The stitching would be done sub-cutaneously (beneath the skin surface) using dissolving sutures, and a drain would be placed in my chest below the incision. The drain would consist of a thin plastic tube with a bag attached, into which the fluid that leaked from the wound would collect. The only dressing on my wound would be a simple pad, held in place by strapping. When the drain was removed I'd be able to go home. The consultant explained that I'd be in hospital for three or four days, and that during that time he would be coming in to see me regularly to check on how I was doing.

He said that after tests had been carried out on the tumour he would be able to tell us whether my cancer was oestrogen receptor positive or genetic. Evidently, it is not usual for breast cancer to be genetic, and only a small percentage originates in this way. But I couldn't help thinking of Lucy, wondering if my having breast cancer meant that she might have an inherited tendency to developing it in the future. It was a terrifying thought that I dismissed almost immediately because I couldn't bear to dwell on it. I prayed that my cancer would be found to be non-genetic.

The breast care nurse asked if there was anything I'd like to talk to her about, at this stage, but the consultant had covered just about everything and I had nothing to ask her. She handed me a couple of leaflets about diet and general information concerning what to expect following a mastectomy, and the meeting came to a close. We got up to leave, thanking the doctor for his kindness and for all he had done thus far to reassure us that everything would be all right. Looking directly into my eyes he said, "The bottom line is we're going to cure this." I knew he was right. He gave me a hug and a polite kiss on my cheek, before shaking Pete's hand warmly, telling us he would see us on Friday. The nurse said goodbye, and we left. I wasn't afraid, because I really believed that I was going to be well, once my breast and the cancer had gone. It had been a satisfying consultation, but I was glad it was over because I wanted to get home and prepare for Lucy and Neal's arrival later on. I knew that in having to keep quiet about my breast cancer my inner strength and moral fibre would be tested to their limits. Lucy is very sensitive to tense atmospheres, and would be able to tell that something was wrong if I didn't do a good enough job in pretending otherwise. Although I was really looking forward to seeing her, at the same time I was also dreading it.

Thirteen

It was mid afternoon when Lucy and Neal arrived. I expected Lucy to be bursting to tell us about their few days away, and was surprised to hear her say that she hadn't been able to enjoy herself. Something, she said, had made her feel uneasy and disturbed the entire time. They'd been camping, the weather had been glorious, and there was no reason at all for Lucy not to have had a good time. She said that even though everything had been perfect she didn't know why she felt so troubled and on edge. I knew, at once. Lucy and I have often been able to sense when one of us has been upset, or something has been wrong, irrespective of geographical distances between us. Since she left home there have been times when I've had a compulsive urge to phone her, only to find her to be distressed or worried about something. She has done likewise, when I've been feeling a similar way. I knew that whilst she was on holiday she had picked up on what was happening here, and that this was why she'd felt so troubled.

When the four of us were out having dinner together that evening I felt very off-balance. Pete and I found it so difficult, laughing and joking with Lucy and Neal, striving to keep what we knew hidden from them. It was terrible. I began to wish we'd told them our news as soon as they'd arrived, and started to question whether our decision to tell Neal first was the correct one. Lucy seemed blissfully happy that evening. It broke my heart to think of how she would react when I told her I had breast cancer. The thought was horrible, and I hated it. I hated myself for having the disease, and for having to tell my daughter about this on her twenty-first birthday. I felt so guilty, but I knew it couldn't be helped.

During the drive home I felt sick. My nerves were on edge, and I began to feel very shaky. I could hardly bring myself to speak. Joining in the conversation was such an effort, and I found it very difficult to relax. Lucy knew I had something on my mind. "Are you all right, Mum?" she had asked several times that evening. "Yes, I'm fine" I lied. The strain was almost unbearable and I detested the situation we were in.

When we arrived home my heart was pounding in my chest. I could hardly think, let alone speak. We had scarcely entered the front door when Lucy announced that she was going to bed. I was so relieved, and after she'd disappeared upstairs I joined Pete and Neal in the living room. Neal looked ashen and very shaken. I knew Pete had told him. The three of us went to sit in the conservatory, where we knew we couldn't be overheard.

Neal gave me a big, warm hug, saying how upset he was to know I'd been diagnosed with breast cancer, but that from what Pete had told him he knew I'd be okay. His feelings were that it would be best if we told Lucy after the birthday celebrations were over, before the two of them went home. He said I should try not to worry about Lucy and should just concentrate on getting well. I felt full of admiration for Neal, and bitterly regretted having placed such a burden upon his shoulders. But because Neal understood our predicament I knew I could forgive myself, and us, for the guilt I was feeling. He was willing to along with our plan, and I was very grateful for his support.

After Neal had gone to bed, Pete and I fell into each other's arms, feeling thoroughly worn-out with the stress we'd been under. In some ways it had been a positive and productive day, but so exhausting emotionally. I went to sleep that night feeling angry and upset at the fact that for the first time in Lucy's life I had been denied the joy and happiness that looking forward to her birthdays had always given me. But in spite of this I was determined to make the most of the special occasion, to enjoy it as best I could under the circumstances, and to make sure the day ended on a positive note. I didn't quite know how this could be achieved, but I knew it would be done somehow. I would just have to play it by ear, depending on how things went. Lucy was now twenty-one years old. The time had come for me to accept that she, after all the years through which I had nurtured and cared for her, was a fully-fledged adult. I was no longer able to kiss her troubles away and make them better like I used to when she was a little girl. Tomorrow, we both would have much growing up to do.

Fourteen

Lucy's birthday was announced by a glorious sunrise. I hadn't slept at all well during the night because my mind persistently dwelled on the heartbreaking task that lay ahead. One of our bedroom windows faces east, and as I gazed out at the golden sky I prayed for inspiration to bless my actions and words today. The sun beamed in, brilliantly illuminating the room, dazzling me. It was so bright that I had to shade my eyes from its glare. I basked in the golden glow, feeling invigorated by it. After a little while, Pete woke. "The sun's shining on you," he said. "On us," I replied. "Today we are going to defy this dark cloud that's been hanging over us, threatening to spoil everything. I'm not going to let it do that." We talked about the day Lucy was born. It didn't feel as if twenty-one years had passed since that happy event, yet here we were, about to celebrate this very fact. We got up, determined to make Lucy's birthday as enjoyable as we could for the four of us and for everyone who would be dropping in to see her during the morning.

I had briefed those who were coming, telling them Lucy knew nothing about my breast cancer, and asking them to keep quiet about it. I knew I'd feel apprehensive when her visitors were here and that I would just have to trust in everyone's integrity. It was horrible to be involved in such deception and I thoroughly regretted not having told Lucy earlier. But there was no going back now, things were proceeding as planned and everyone was in agreement about it. My conscience was screaming the word "guilt" at me, over and over again. I hoped Lucy would understand why we hadn't told her about my breast cancer yesterday, and that she would forgive us for this.

Unfortunately the bracelet didn't fit, and we decided that after the visitors had been and gone we would take Lucy out to exchange it. I welcomed the thought of getting away from home for a while. Neal said he would take us all in his car, and with this in mind I began to relax. Everything was going according to plan, and there was a light-hearted and happy atmosphere in the house. Pete and I could hardly believe that we'd successfully managed to behave as though everything was normal. I was so enjoying Lucy's birthday that at times I almost forgot that later on I would have to tell her I had breast cancer.

Visitors came and went, and at lunchtime my friend Sue arrived. Sue and I have known each other since childhood. Her daughter Tracy has been Lucy's close friend since the two of them were small. As I welcomed Sue I remembered Tracy's twenty-first birthday party, which the four of us had enjoyed a month ago. It had been such a happy occasion, and I bitterly resented the fact that Lucy's joy on this her own special birthday was soon to be shattered. Sue and I spoke briefly together in the hall before she went in to see Lucy. She told me not to worry because although she was feeling very upset about our situation she wouldn't give the game away. We hugged each other. I thanked her for her understanding and willingness to co-operate. She knew I would have done the same for her, if the situation had been reversed. I knew I could trust Sue as together we went into the living room. Lucy was so pleased to see her, and she stayed for almost an hour before leaving to return to work. On her way out she hugged me again, saying "I love you Chris, good luck and well done." We both cried then, in each other's arms. I told her not to worry about me because I would be fine after the mastectomy, and we said goodbye. As she waved to me from the gate Sue looked much happier than she had done when she arrived, and her lovely smile was one positive mental image I intended to take with me when I went into hospital in a couple of days' time.

After lunch the four of us set off on the expedition to exchange the bracelet. Pete and I sat together in the back of Neal's car. Lucy was laughing and chatting, oblivious to everything but her happiness. Music was playing on the car stereo and it was hot and sunny. A perfect day for any young woman to celebrate her twenty-first, enjoying the company of the people she loves and looking forward to her future. Pete squeezed my hand whenever I looked at him. I felt terrible, knowing what had yet to be done. Neal had been terrific all through the day. Pete and I both realised how apprehensive he must have felt as the time for telling Lucy drew nearer. We both admired Neal for the strength he exhibited, and wished we could have spared him the responsibility we had placed with him. It couldn't have been at all easy for him not to give anything away. As we drove along I continually wondered what was going on in Neal's head. Eventually I preferred not to even try to imagine it.

The small shop was full of Celtic jewellery, crystals, ornaments, and many beautiful things. Lucy soon found another bracelet that fitted her better. The exchange was made and we drove home. The birthday cake had yet to be cut and we all decided to have a piece with a cup of tea. Neal flopped onto the sofa, looking very tired and drawn, closing his eyes. I knew his anxiety had overcome him, and he later told us that the only way he had been able to cope with the prospect of us telling Lucy about me was to lie down and shut his eyes for a while. The tension had become too much for him and he needed to escape from it. This we understood all too well. For Neal, the strain of keeping up a show of pretence for so many hours had eventually become intolerable.

Lucy cut her cake, giving us each a slice. I felt so worked up that I could hardly eat mine. After a couple of minutes I looked across the room at Pete. He'd finished his cake. So had Neal. Lucy was almost through hers. I swallowed hard. I could scarcely breathe, and the cake stuck in my throat. After a few more minutes, Pete looked straight at me, then at Neal, then back at me. I knew the time had come.

"Lucy," Pete said, "Mum's got something to tell you." Neal, turning white, stared blankly at the fireplace. "What?" Lucy asked, looking at me with a quizzical expression. "What's wrong, Mum?" Her carefree mood vanished at once as she sensed something was amiss. Her face wore an expression of bewilderment. I felt absolutely awful, wretched and desperately miserable as I searched for the right words. Summoning all my strength, I began to explain. "I have to go into hospital on Friday. I've got a breast lump." Lucy's face was now full of fear. "Just what do you mean Mum?" I was almost in pieces as I continued. "The lump has been diagnosed as being malignant and on Friday I'm having a mastectomy." "Oh God Mum, you mean it's cancer?" "Yes, I'm afraid so. But it's not as bad as it could be," I added hastily, clutching at my one and only straw. "My consultant says he's confident that the mastectomy will get rid of it all." "Oh Mum, oh God!" Lucy cried. She ran across the room and collapsed at my feet, her arms hugging my legs, and burying her face in my lap she sobbed as if her heart would break. All I could do was just hold her. Nobody said anything for a while. I glanced across at Pete, who was also crying, and at Neal, who appeared to be on the verge of doing so. Looking down at Lucy again I stroked her hair. She lifted her tear-stained face to look up into mine, and at that moment I could see all the ages she had ever been; the baby, the young child, the teenager, and the woman she now was. The faces of all the past ages of my lovely daughter seemed to have merged and blended into one beautiful but utterly grief-stricken countenance. Holding her face gently in my hands I kissed it, and asked her to listen to the rest of what I had to say because it would reassure and comfort her. Lucy returned my kiss and went back to sit next to Neal on the sofa.

Pete took over then, explaining everything to Lucy carefully and thoroughly. When she knew I'd gone for scans in February she was horrified, and she was also upset because we hadn't told her anything about this. I explained that we felt there was no reason for us to mention it at that time, because the scans all showed that everything was normal. As parents we try never to worry our child with our problems. In February Lucy was struggling to keep up with her work at university. The last thing she needed then was the anxiety our telling her I had a breast lump would have caused.

Suddenly, Lucy exclaimed that she now knew why she hadn't enjoyed herself on holiday, realising what it was that had been responsible for the black mood and heavy feelings she experienced whilst away. She was certain she'd picked up on the trauma Pete and I were going through. Then, remembering that she and Neal were intending to visit his family at the weekend, Lucy said she didn't want to go. Instead she wanted to be here when I went into hospital. I insisted she went as planned, stressing how important it was for me to feel happy and positive when I was in hospital. If Lucy's meeting with Neal's family had to be postponed because of my operation it would make me feel miserable. I told her that there was nothing she could do here, and that if she came home for a few days when I was out of hospital, that would be more helpful to her dad and me. Reluctantly Lucy agreed to go, saying she would come to see us as soon as she and Neal returned.

By this time it was late afternoon. Lucy and Neal were set to leave in a couple of hours. I wanted the day to end on a cheerful note and had an idea. "Right," I said, that's the bad news over with. Now I'm taking the dog for a walk. When I get back I want to see that old computer of ours out and you all playing a game on it, okay?" I left the room, hoping my words would have the desired effect. It had all been so heavy going and we needed to have some fun together before Lucy and Neal went home. Something happy, in which we could all share.

I stayed out with the dog for half an hour. Although the feeling of unreality still bore down on me it was combined with tremendous relief. Lucy knew about my breast cancer at last. I felt a sense of achievement in having been able to deal with the problem so capably, on this of all days. When I got home I found Pete, Neal and Lucy all enjoying themselves playing a pinball game. They were having a great time, which was what I'd longed to see. Everyone was smiling. "Come on Chrissie, you have a go" urged Neal. I joined in the fun, so glad I'd thought of this idea. It had produced the result I wanted. The atmosphere was just like Christmas, the family together and all having fun. I couldn't have asked for more.

When it was time for them to go, Lucy became quiet and thoughtful. Pete and I left the pair alone for a few minutes, and when I went back into the living room I found them hugging each other. Neal beckoned me to join in. "I'm proud to part of this family" he declared. I was so full of emotion that I couldn't speak. I just hugged the two of them as tightly as I could, knowing that this was a moment I would never forget.

Saying goodbye that night was very difficult. Before they left, Neal gave us the telephone numbers of various members of his family so that we would be able to contact Lucy while she was away. Watching their car as it turned the corner of our road and disappeared from sight, I felt inwardly peaceful. I knew that although Lucy would be very worried about me, she would be all right. We stepped back indoors and went straight to bed.

Before I went to sleep I reflected on the day. Lucy's twenty-first had turned out to be a huge milestone, not only in her life but in our lives too. It had been a true Rite of Passage in every sense of the word. A day of very mixed emotions, this was one birthday none of us would ever forget. I was thankful for the strength I'd been given, and for the love of my family, both of which had upheld me. Now, it was time to embark on the next stage of my journey forward into battle with my cancer, and to prepare myself for the mastectomy in two days' time.

Fifteen

Next morning when I woke I held my left breast and felt the lump. Ever since the diagnosis I'd left it alone because there was no point in trying to detect changes any more. Today I wanted to touch it, and I believe that subconsciously I was bidding it farewell, acknowledging its imminent departure from my body. As I washed I looked at it in the mirror. The difference between it and my other one was startling and blatantly obvious. I disliked it intensely and couldn't wait to be rid of it.

This was my last day with two breasts, and I gave a great deal of thought to this as I studied myself in the mirror. Lately I'd got into the habit of holding the affected one to the side, flattening it, trying to envisage how I'd look without it. I did so now, thinking it didn't look so bad, that I could get used to looking like this. For the first time, I showed Pete what I'd been doing, wanting him to see how I might look after the operation. Pity was written all over his face as he put his arms around me. "My darling, I don't have any problem with that. You're too lovely for that to make any difference to me. The main thing is I still have YOU, and that's all I want." I thought how lucky I was to have a man like Pete for my husband. Like any other couple that have been together a long time, we've had our ups and downs. What was happening to us now only seemed to be strengthening the relationship we had both thought was as solid as it could ever be. The bond between us had grown even stronger because of this crisis we were facing. It seemed almost miraculous that such depth of loving, feeling and caring could arise from something as devastating as the traumatic experience we were going through.

The day seemed to pass incredibly slowly, and this frustrated me because I wanted to pack my bag. I only needed to take a few things to hospital, and there was no point in packing too early. I had very little to do at all that day, except wait for tomorrow to arrive. I'd got all our washing up to date, and made sure there was enough food in the house to last while I was away, although Pete told me not to worry about this because he could easily shop for himself. He often does the shopping for us, and we've always shared the household chores. I knew he'd be fine when I was in hospital, and thought how lucky I was to have a man who has never expected me to do everything for him, and who has always looked after us when I've been unwell or unable to manage things for any reason. He didn't deserve what was happening to us now.

As the hours ticked by I became more and more agitated. I wanted to get on with having the mastectomy and the waiting was awful. I felt no dread or fear when I thought about the operation, because I realised it would save my life, and was glad to be having it. Just as a bad tooth causes so much discomfort and pain that it is a relief to have it taken out, so was I relieved that my unhealthy breast was soon going to be taken away from my body. I saw no point in being afraid because I knew there would be far more for me to fear if I wasn't going through this. I visualised an army of beautiful, single-breasted Amazons, cheering me on, yelling their battle cries and screaming words of encouragement, and felt safe.

Several well-wishers telephoned during the day. It was good to know we were being thought of, and we appreciated every call. Each one meant such a lot to us. Offers of help following my operation came from every direction. We were far from alone. It was as though everyone we knew was encouraging and supporting us as we prepared for our battle. Allies, on our side against the enemy.

In the evening I asked Pete to help me pack my bag. I wanted him to be involved, and asked him what he thought I'd need. I didn't want him to feel excluded from any part of what was going on. We packed the usual things, nightie, slippers, dressing gown, toiletries, notebook and pen, and some photographs. One of our garden, another that Sue had given me, of Lucy, Neal, Pete and myself taken at Tracy's twenty-first birthday party. I wanted to have with me a photo of us all as a happy family, and this one was perfect. Turning to our Silver Wedding album I selected one of us both, taken during the ceremony of renewal of our marriage vows, held at sunset in the great temple of Stonehenge in June 1998. In a flash I re-lived the ceremony in my mind, remembering the beauty of it and how very moving it was, recalling Pete saying he had never experienced anything as meaningful and relevant to life. In particular I remembered that one of the vows we made was to love and honour each other through periods of uncertainty and when problems appear immovable. This was indeed one of those times. The photograph showed us looking into each other's eyes, our faces full of emotion, and I knew it was the right one for me to take, that it would fortify and uphold me while I was in hospital. In went my chunk of rose quartz, which I wanted to have beside my bed. Rose quartz is a crystal associated with warming the heart, supporting one's capacity to love what one is, and through this to aid self-healing. A precious gift of Nature bestowed through the medium of Earth, it meant a great deal for me to have this lovely object with me. Finally I put in a card Ray had sent. It bore a simple message of three words that I found particularly significant and incredibly empowering. "Courage, brave Amazon" he had written.

As I closed the bag I thought, "This is it. I am ready".

Before we turned in, Pete and I went out into the garden. It was a lovely evening, peaceful and tranquil, with only the mere hint of a breeze. We entered our stone circle and stood either side of the tree stump in the centre, facing each other, the silence broken only by the whispering leaves on the branches of the cherry tree. One branch reached over our heads, like a hand with its fingers extended in a gesture of blessing. Pete held my hands in his over the stump, as we shared the beauty and sanctity of the moment. Earlier, he told me he needed me to believe that he would always love me despite what was going to happen to my body. All he wanted was for me to be here with him, so that we could carry on doing the things we enjoy together. Nothing else mattered to him. And so it was that on the eve of my mastectomy we went forward into the, as yet, unknown with mutual trust and determination that we would confront this formidable foe which threatened our future, and that together we would defeat it.

Sixteen

During the drive to hospital I didn't want to talk about the operation at all. I had a positive mind-set and wanted to chat about something other than that. For an entire week Pete and I had spoken of nothing else, and now we needed a bit of relief from the subject of my breast cancer and the mastectomy. We talked casually about run-of-the-mill, everyday things as we drove along, just as we normally do when we go out together, and in no time at all we were in the hospital car park.

Pete carried my bag as we walked the short distance to the door of reception. The receptionist greeted us and we checked in. My consultant and a nurse appeared as we took our seats in the waiting area. He shook our hands, asking if we felt okay. The nurse had to take a blood sample for routine preliminary tests prior to the surgery. The consultant told me he would see me after it was all over, and wished me well. After the blood was taken we were shown to my room.

Two nurses greeted us as we entered. One said she would be looking after me before and after the operation. She made sure I knew where everything was before handing me a hospital gown and a pair of white elastic knee length stockings. Patients have to wear these to help prevent blood clotting in the leg veins after surgery. The nurses left the room and I undressed, putting on the gown, which was open at the front, followed by the stockings. I unpacked my things and Pete put my clothes in the bag to take home with him. I stuck the photographs onto the bedside cabinet where I could easily see them. When my nurse returned I asked her if Pete would be able to stay with me until after the operation. She smiled, saying of course he could stay, for as long as we both wished. Pete sat on the armchair beside my bed. I was so glad to know he would be with me the whole time. The nurse chatted to us for a few minutes, mentioning that she'd had breast cancer several years ago. I took notice of how well she looked now, determined that I would make it, just as she had done. The nurse explained all about the procedures leading up to the operation, putting us at ease, and when she left the room Pete asked if I felt all right. He looked concerned for me but I told him not to worry because I felt fine.

A smiling young man popped his head around the door, asking me what I'd like to eat and drink after the operation was over. I asked for egg sandwiches and a cup of tea. Then a different nurse came in to check my blood pressure and temperature. I remember thinking, "There's no going back now," as I glanced at the clock on the wall. It was almost nine a.m. The mastectomy was scheduled to begin at eleven. In two hours the operation to remove my breast, and with it the cancer, would be underway. I detested having to wait and just longed for it to be all over. I felt hungry and thirsty but wasn't permitted to eat or drink anything before the surgery. I was really looking forward to those sandwiches and tea!

After a while the anaesthetist came to see us. He introduced himself and explained that he would be there to meet me on my arrival at the operating theatre. His professionalism inspired confidence in me. I knew I was going to be in safe hands. Soon after ten my nurse came to offer me a pre-med. This is tranquillising medication, given to relax a patient prior to their surgery if they feel they would like it. I wanted the pre-med and was given a couple of tablets that I swallowed gladly, looking forward to their effect. I hoped I'd feel drowsy before I went to the operating theatre, knowing it would make things easier for me and help prevent sudden panic striking me at the last moment. I've had several operations in the past and knew what to expect from the pre-med. The clock ticked on and soon it was eleven. Pete was holding my hand, talking to me all the while. I began to feel concerned as the time passed, but the nurse explained that there had been a bit of a delay and it wouldn't be long before the porter came to take me to the theatre. I closed my eyes and tried to sleep, but couldn't. Despite the pre-med my tension was building. I breathed deeply, and had just begun to drift into a more peaceful state of relaxation when I heard a different voice. "Good morning Mrs. Rayner, I've come to take you to the operating theatre." Opening my eyes, I saw the friendly face of the porter and felt my bed start to move. Pete kissed me, and as I looked up into his face I felt like crying. "See you when you come back, my darling" he whispered, giving my hand a squeeze. "I love you," I murmured. "I love you too" he replied, his voice breaking with emotion, "you'll be all right. I'll be here waiting for you, don't worry about anything." I held the vision of Pete's dear face behind my closed eyelids all the time as I was wheeled to the theatre. It was the only thing I wanted to see.

As my bed came to an abrupt halt I opened my eyes. Standing there was the anaesthetist, looking altogether very different from when I had met him earlier. Then, he had been wearing a casual tweed jacket. Now he was in a gown, cap and mask. I was in the recovery area next to the operating theatre. "Hello again Mrs. Rayner. I'm going to insert a needle into the back of your hand. Just try to relax." I felt a slight pressure but no pain. There were no feelings of panic or fear. Just peace. The anaesthetist said, "Now I'm going to give you something to make you feel a little more relaxed". The next thing I heard was another voice, female. It was my nurse. "Christine, it's all over. You've been very brave".

Seventeen

I was back in my room and although very drowsy I was aware of a lot of activity going on around me. Pete was stroking my head. I saw his face, heard his voice, felt his touch, and realised I had made it. The mastectomy was done.

A couple of nurses were with us and I heard one say "We're just raising the end of your bed". My blood pressure was very low and the foot of my bed was lifted to help restore it to normal. My fingers were tingling and I felt weak and light-headed. The anaesthetic had caused my blood pressure to fall, and it took some time for it to normalise and for the tingling in my hands to stop. I vaguely remember babbling, "I love you all!" as the nurses worked around me, and Pete told me afterwards that this raised a few smiles. As one nurse leaned over me to check my eyes I slurred, "You've got a lovely face," in a tone that in any other situation might have given the impression that I'd been having rather too much fun at a party, instead of a surgical operation! For a brief moment I believe I thought this nurse was an angel. Anaesthesia can have a strange effect on our perceptions. She happened to be the sister in charge, and when I'd recovered my full senses later on I apologised to her for any embarrassment my remark may have caused. She laughed and told me to think no more of it because she was used to hearing patients say all kinds of things as they recovered from their anaesthesia.

My mouth and lips felt dry and I wanted some water, but was only allowed small sips through a straw. Pete held the glass for me. The coolness of the water was fabulous. After I was given injections to relieve pain and sickness I began to feel very tired, and soon drifted into a deep, relaxing sleep.

It was around seven o'clock in the evening when I woke up. The first thing I did was to look for Pete. A nurse said he'd gone home shortly after I'd dropped off. The staff had told him that I'd be asleep for several hours and that he might as well go and get some well earned rest himself. I understood how exhausted Pete must have been, and looked forward to speaking to him on the phone later. The sandwiches and tea arrived and I couldn't wait to get them down. That first cup of tea after an operation is the best thing in the world! I felt serene. The surgery was over, and now all I had to do was recover from it. It was a marvellous feeling.

After I'd had my supper two nurses came in with a commode chair. Being still a little dozy I needed help to get out of bed. I couldn't wait to be able to get to the bathroom by myself and was determined that tomorrow I would do so. For now, the indignity of having to use the commode was far outweighed by the relief it brought! I was linked up to a drip, which fed into a vein in the back of my hand, and the drainage tube protruded from my chest just below breast level. I'd expected to be in pain when I moved around, but the discomfort wasn't too severe because of the painkilling injection I'd had earlier. It is very important to move about as soon as possible after most operations, to get the blood circulating and so help prevent clotting and other complications. I was glad to be up and mobile. I didn't want to feel like an invalid and was determined to get back to normal as soon as I could.

Once back in bed I asked a nurse when I'd be able to look at my chest to see what my consultant had done. She told me that in a couple of days my wound would be cleaned and I could see it then if I wished. There was no "if" about it, I wanted to see the place where my breast had been, and at the earliest opportunity. For me it was important to see it as soon as possible. I wanted to accept the scar, to welcome it into my life. I intended to honour it, to regard it symbolically as a kind of medal, one I'd fought hard to win and that I would wear with pride. I couldn't wait to look, and as soon as I was alone I had a sneaky peep beneath the dressing. It was imperative for me to see what I looked like sooner rather than later, so that I could begin to come to terms with my new appearance.

I couldn't see much because the strapping was fixed so well to the pad, but what I could see was enough to reassure me that I would look okay when everything was healed and that there was little for me to worry about on that score. I lay back on my pillow, deep in thought. I was consumed with an overwhelming feeling of gratitude for my life, and sheer joy at being alive. I saw the mastectomy as a reason to be joyful, because the cancer had been removed. I felt no sadness whatsoever at the loss of my breast, because I realised that I needed to suffer this loss in order to gain the best chance of life, and I'd got this into perspective from day one. After the sneak preview I was content, proud at having taken that first vital step towards full acceptance of what had happened to me. At that memorable moment in my life I felt full of self-confidence and strength, able to regard the loss of my breast objectively. It was extraordinary. Never had I felt as strong as I did at that moment. I gave the dressing an appreciative pat and settled down to watch the TV.

An episode of 'Fawlty Towers' was being shown, which was opportune because I love this programme and enjoyed the humour. The laughter did me good and I found it hard to believe that only a few hours after having a mastectomy I was sitting up and enjoying my favourite TV comedy show. I was so relieved to know that my breast and the cancer it bore was now gone. Placing my hand over the dressing I whispered my gratitude to my unseen guardians, knowing I had been protected and well looked after.

I desperately needed to speak to Pete and after the programme finished I rang for the nurse, asking her to bring me a telephone. I shook with excitement as the anticipation of Pete's reaction to hearing me on the other end of the phone built up. I knew he would be thrilled that I felt strong enough to give him a call, and my fingers trembled as I dialled our number. I was impatient as I listened to the ringing tone, longing for him to answer. When he did, my tears overflowed. They were tears of joy and absolute relief, not of sorrow or despair. It was wonderful for us to be speaking to each other.

I assured Pete that I felt fine in both body and mind when he told me he'd been concerned that, when I regained my full awareness after the operation, I might feel devastated at what had happened to me. Nothing could have been further from the truth, and this came as good news for Pete. I chatted to him non-stop, describing my evening thus far, telling him everything, sparing no detail however small. I wanted him to feel he was still an important part of what was happening, even though the operation was now over. I sensed that I had some way to go yet, and I wanted Pete to know how very much I appreciated his support. I also needed to tell him I realised that everything that was happening to me was affecting him too.

Pete said he couldn't wait to see me, that he'd come and visit me early next day, and we wished each other goodnight. I felt so full of love for him, the mature, long-established kind of love that is the product of having shared bad times as well as good, of having been there for each other through all the trials, tribulations, disasters and heartaches that inevitably come to pass during a span of almost three decades. Together we'd fought another battle and emerged from it victorious. I didn't feel sorry for us, or for myself. Pete and I had nothing to feel sorry about. We knew how lucky we were just to have each other. Talking to him had inspired me to carry on feeling positive and confident that all would be well, for this was what Pete truly believed. I settled down to sleep, content in knowing that my initiation into the Amazon Sisterhood was complete. I had passed the test of endurance for which I'd been preparing myself during the past seven long days, and when I'd pointed my arrow at the heart of the cancer my aim had been straight, good and true.

Eighteen

At six-thirty next morning I phoned Pete again. He was both surprised and relieved to hear me on the other end of the line because he thought such an early call might mean something was wrong. He said I sounded very chirpy and relaxed, and that he was really pleased to know I was still feeling fine. He wanted to hear every detail about what was going on. I told him I'd had a good night, been given a cup of tea at six a.m. and had some painkillers. All I wanted to know was how he was. He said he'd slept soundly all night, after a very busy afternoon and evening. Evidently the phone hadn't stopped ringing, and he reeled off a score of names of people who had called to ask how I was doing after the surgery. I thought this must have been a good morale-booster for Pete. Although talking to so many people had been tiring, the sincerity of their interest had cheered him. We were blessed to have so many good, loving thoughts and prayers with us.

We couldn't wait to see each other and Pete said he'd be there as soon as he could. The dog needed walking and there were a few things for him to do first. I told him I'd be happy when he got here but insisted he didn't rush and tear around. I just wanted him to take his time and not hurry, and made him promise to take it easy. We said goodbye to each other cheerfully. The conversation had been relaxed, unhurried, and mutually heartening. Lying back on my pillows I felt a glow of satisfaction, knowing that Pete and I were both in such good spirits. Things no longer felt unreal. The reality was that I'd had the mastectomy and was now recovering from it. It felt good to be back on the planet!

Breakfast arrived at eight o'clock, and then I had to wash. The nurse asked if I'd like a bowl of warm water brought to my bed but I wanted to use the washbasin. I got out of bed by myself but needed the nurse to help me to the small bathroom adjoining my room. It was an effort but I was determined to get there. That commode, I vowed, would be a one-off! The brief encounter I'd had with it the night before was enough for me, and as far as I was concerned our association was now terminated.

I felt very weak and still a little dopey, so the nurse helped me wash as I sat on the closed lid of the loo. Tubes from the drip and the drain got in the way at first but I soon got used to working around them. I thought it would be wonderful to be able to have a shower or bath after these things had been removed. In the meantime I had to be content with soap and a flannel. I missed the luxury of shower gel and the feel of water running down over my body. But at least I felt clean and fresh afterwards, and I was grateful to the nurse for her help. Just as we were finishing there came a knock on the bathroom door. It was the anaesthetist, coming to see if I felt all right after the operation. He was very sweet, saying he was pleased to see me up and about. I thanked him for looking after me throughout the surgical procedure. Anaesthetists carry an enormous responsibility and I was extremely grateful to this doctor for his care, and also the way in which he'd put me at my ease prior to the surgery. His visit was a fleeting one, and when he'd gone the nurse got me back into my bed. The next thing was to choose what I wanted to eat that day. One item on the menu immediately caught my eye. Strawberry meringue, offered as a sweet after the evening meal. I placed an emphatic tick against that one and began looking forward to it right away!

Flowers started arriving, which was lovely. Pete walked in just as some from my sister Liz were being delivered. He had brought me an enormous bouquet, and several greetings cards people had asked him to give me. I was overwhelmed, and it was wonderful to see him. It felt as though we'd been apart for ages, and we had such a lot to say to each other. He sat on the chair next to my bed, saying he couldn't get over how well I looked. I did feel extremely well although still tired, and Pete understood when I needed to doze off now and again. He was just happy to be there by my side, and when I closed my eyes he had little naps too. All we wanted was to be together and it didn't matter that we spent some of the time sleeping. We both felt such relief, that the surgery had been carried out and all had gone well. Now was the time for us to catch up on our rest. The nursing staff were very kind to Pete, making sure he was supplied with cups of tea and coffee, reassuring him that he wasn't in the way and could stay with me for as long as he wanted. We were both touched by their caring attitude, which was as much for us as a couple as it was for me, the patient. Nothing seemed to be too much trouble for them. Their dedication to their profession was outstanding.

Pete looked completely shattered. He was suffering badly with stress, and his doctor had signed him off work for a couple of weeks, saying that the stress was understandable because we were dealing with something unknown. We still had to be told the results of the tests on my cancer, and Pete was finding this difficult to think about. He has a responsible job and it was all too much for him to handle at this time of uncertainty and anxiety. His bosses understood and were very sympathetic, telling him not to worry and that they would manage without him until he felt well enough to return. The people he works with were brilliant. Phone calls with good wishes came from every quarter, and Pete was moved to tears as he told me about the concern of his managers and workmates for me, and for us. Situations like the one we were in tend to bring out the inherent goodness in people, and everyone was so very kind.

Around mid-morning we had a visitor. It was the breast care nurse, who had come to show me some exercises I needed to do to help restore full movement to my left arm. During a mastectomy the muscles of the chest take a battering, and with all the stitching everything feels very tight and uncomfortable, although not really painful as such. But there is a need for regular exercising, which has to be done twice daily for several weeks or months in order to remedy the discomfort and enable the arm to gradually recover its full extent of movement. There were half a dozen exercises, involving gentle stretching, that I could begin doing straight away. I was eager to get started, and went through each one under the nurse's supervision. One involved facing the wall and placing the fingers of both hands on it at waist height to begin with, then crawling the fingers up the wall until the pain threshold was reached. "I can easily do this," I thought. Wrong! I could barely get my left hand up to the level of my shoulder. I was surprised at the limited movement in my arm and resolved to do these exercises meticulously because I wanted to get over this hurdle as soon as possible. The others involved performing actions such as pretending to do up a bra, or pressing the palms of the hands together, and although I found these slightly easier, they were still tricky because of the tightness under my arm and in my chest.

After going through them all with me the nurse asked for my assurance that I would do them every day, morning and night, without fail. She didn't need to ask twice!

The other thing the nurse spoke to me about was lymphoedema. After lymph glands have been removed during breast surgery there may sometimes be a problem with lymph drainage. It can collect in the tissues in the arm, causing swelling and tightness. Heavy lifting and other energetic activities that involve putting pressure on the affected arm must be avoided otherwise lymphoedema can be a real problem. The arm can become very big and sometimes never returns to its original size. There are various methods of controlling lymphoedema but the risk of developing it is there for life, not just after surgery. Fortunately I have never been affected by this complaint, because I am always careful to lift heavy things with my other arm. But I knew that unless I kept my arms toned they would go flabby, especially as I had exercised with weights for a long time before I developed breast cancer, and I wondered how I would be able to maintain my arm suppleness without putting myself at risk of getting lymphoedema. I sought advice from my breast specialist about this. It is sensible to ask the consultant or breast care nurse before attempting to do anything that might cause problems with the affected arm, and never to take chances or think "It won't matter just this once". Sometimes once is enough, and then the problem may be there for life.

Pete returned just as the nurse was leaving. She said she'd be back to see me in a couple of days to give me a soft breast form (known, appropriately, as a 'softie') that I'd be able to wear in my bras until my scar had completely healed. After that I'd be given a permanent, silicone-filled one. I wondered how I'd get on with such a thing, whether it would look lifelike and feel comfortable. The nurse said we'd have plenty of time to discuss this when I saw her again. Pete sat down and asked what she'd had to say. I showed him a leaflet she'd given me about the exercises I had to do. He took a keen interest, saying we could watch my progress together. It was nice to feel his involvement. I knew Pete was as eager for me to get my arm back to normal as I was, because he realised how much this would mean to me.

He had scarcely been back half an hour before I began to feel uncomfortable with an attack of abdominal pain. This became so severe that I could hardly move, and I knew it was a bad attack of trapped wind! The same thing has happened in the past, after other operations I've had. The pain was agonising and nothing could be done to relieve it, even though the nurses brought me all kinds of pills and potions to try to disperse the bubble of gas trapped under my diaphragm. I writhed around but couldn't get myself into a comfortable position at all. I was very upset because I'd wanted to spend the day enjoying Pete's company, and because the pain was so acute I eventually couldn't even talk to him. Lunch arrived, but I didn't want to eat anything. The pain just refused to ease and I was in terrible discomfort. In the end I told Pete he might as well go home, there was nothing he could do for me, I'd just have to wait until the wind dispersed and the pain abated. Reluctantly he left, saying he'd be in to see me early next morning. I cried as we said goodbye, but all I really wanted to do was sleep, hoping the pain would be gone when I woke up.

More antacids were given to me during the evening but nothing worked. I still couldn't face eating anything and refused dinner. I managed to sleep on and off, and in between naps I staggered around, trying to shift the trapped wind. Later on a doctor looked in. He prescribed a pill, and the relief was almost immediate. I was so grateful for this, but wished I could have had the tablet earlier . . . . I'd missed that strawberry meringue!

Nineteen

I was in hospital for four days altogether. Pete came to see me every day, bringing with him flowers and cards on each visit. Eventually so many flowers arrived that the vases had to be stood on the floor because every available space was filled with them. My room looked like a florist's shop and the colours were absolutely beautiful. I felt surrounded by love as each day I read the words on all my cards, and looked at the gorgeous flowers from family, friends and neighbours. Reading peoples' words of kindness and encouragement, seeing how much they cared, made me even more determined to be strong and positive. My thinking was focused on getting out and about again, letting everyone see and know that I was all right. I held this thought in my mind all the time, and I feel certain that it was instrumental in enabling me to recover so quickly from the operation. The excitement generated by the prospect of seeing everyone when I got out of hospital was inspiring, and motivated me to really concentrate on doing everything I could to help myself heal and restore my body to its normal state as soon as possible.

The exercises went well. I did everything the breast care nurse had shown me, and even after just a couple of days I could move my left arm more easily. Pete was thrilled to see my mobility improving. I enjoyed watching his surprised reactions when I showed him how much further I could raise my arm each day. As it rose higher and higher, so did our spirits. We knew it wouldn't be long before I was back to normal, and the relaxed expression on Pete's face told me how relieved he was to see me improving at a constant rate.

To help pass the time we played card games, especially Patience. One of the nurses showed me a different version of it, which soon became addictive. I couldn't stop playing it, and when Pete came to see me I demonstrated how it worked. From then on it was all we did! We became engrossed, enjoying it so much that we played it together for months after I came out of hospital. The nurse was pleased when I told her she deserved full marks for entertainment value!

When Pete wasn't with me I took short strolls up and down the corridor outside my room, to get some exercise. This became much easier after my drip was taken out, although the drain was still in place and I had to carry the bag as I walked. Instead of my own nightie I wore a hospital gown that fastened with tapes at the back. On one occasion I tottered up and down the corridor chatting to staff, visitors and other patients, blissfully unaware that although the tape at the neck of my gown was tied, the rest had come undone, giving everyone behind me an excellent view of my knickers! One of the nurses noticed this, rushed up to me and tied the other tapes firmly. I saw the funny side of it, thinking how fortunate it was for everyone that I'd been wearing some at all.

On the third night as I was taking a pre-bedtime stroll, I passed the open door of a room containing an elderly patient. This lady spotted me and, thinking I was a nurse, called me to her, demanding a bedpan! It was obvious that her need was urgent when she began to wail "I'm starting to go, I'm starting to go . . ." Astonished at the speed at which I suddenly found myself able to move, I hurried to the nurses' office, where a meeting was in progress. The volume of the old dear's wailing had intensified, and I hammered loudly on the door before entering the room and describing her plight. The scene in that office, which when I went in had been calm and business-like, changed in a split second to one of sheer mayhem. Mugs of coffee were slammed down, their contents splashing over the table, papers (those that weren't saturated with coffee) flew into the air, chairs toppled over, plastic aprons were snatched from a pile on a shelf, the rest slipping and sliding onto the floor, yards of blue absorbent paper were wrenched from a roll on the wall, and I was left standing in what can only be described as something resembling the aftermath of a small tornado. I glanced down the corridor in the direction of the old lady's room, just in time to see the perpetrators of this chaos disappearing into it. Suddenly, my attention was diverted by the sound of a thunderous clattering noise coming from the opposite direction. As I turned to look, the commode chair, which appeared to have taken on a life of its own, whizzed by at an alarming speed, with a panting, red-faced little nursing auxiliary in tow. I watched, fascinated, as chair and nurse also vanished into the room. The wailing subsided, and everything went quiet. I went back to my room feeling as though I'd just witnessed the rehearsal of a scene from a 'Carry On' film.

After about forty-five minutes I made my way stealthily back along the corridor, which was by this time silent and deserted. Passing the nurses' office I peeped through the small window in the door. The meeting had been reconvened. It was as if nothing had happened. I wondered if I'd dreamed the whole thing. Continuing on to the end of the corridor I came to the old lady's room. Her door was still open. I peered round it, trying not to make a noise in case she was sleeping. She was wide-awake, sitting up in bed and looking at a magazine. "Are you all right now?" I asked. "Yes, thank you. Goodnight Nurse."

Twenty

The consultant came to see me several times after the operation, telling me he was very pleased with my progress and saying that when the drain was removed I could go home. I was longing to be rid of the drain and its accompanying bag. The pair of them had begun to feel as if they were part of my body. When I walked around I had to carry the bag, its gruesome-looking contents on display for all to see. The fluid it contained was yellowish, bloodstained, and not at all a pretty sight. Whenever I did my exercises I had to place the bag on a chair next to me, to enable me to have two free hands. When I washed, I put it on the lid of the loo. When I was in bed it rested on a low stool on the floor. I was really looking forward to having it taken out and being able to move around unencumbered again.

On the third morning I was sitting in the armchair reading a paper when a nurse came in to clean my wound. She asked me to get on the bed, saying it would make things easier for her and less uncomfortable for me. I felt a pang of apprehension at the thought of seeing my chest fully uncovered for the first time, but I was ready for it. The nurse asked me if I wanted to look or preferred not to, at this stage, and I told her I felt fine about seeing it. I regarded this as a challenge that I was determined to meet, trusting that my Amazonian strength would fortify me enough to be able to withstand what might initially prove to be a shocking and perhaps distressing experience, even though I was confident that I would handle it well. With bated breath I watched the nurse's every move as she carefully pulled away the strapping and gently lifted off the pad.

The cut extended from the middle of my chest to below my armpit, just as the surgeon said it would. It was surprisingly neat, the dissolving sutures being concealed beneath the surface of the skin. There was naturally some bruising, with a slight swelling along the line of the incision, otherwise it all looked very good, much better and more pleasing than I'd expected. I felt glad to have seen it because now I knew I could allow myself to heal emotionally as well as physically.

The nurse wiped the wound, cleaning it thoroughly. Before she replaced the dressing I asked her to give me a few more moments to take it all in. She held my hand, noticing the tears that had started to spill over. The emotion had overwhelmed me. But I wasn't at all mournful. I felt calm and happy, thankful that I'd come through all this feeling stronger than I can ever remember feeling in my entire life. After a minute or two I told the nurse I was satisfied, and the dressing was replaced. Thanking her for her understanding, I settled down to wait for Pete. I was bursting to tell him I'd seen my scar and that it looked so neat. Psychologically the experience had given me a real boost, because I'd been able to physically see that I was on the road to recovery.

Later the breast care nurse came to give me the softie, a breast-shaped pouch made of soft, skin-toned cotton material, with a hole in one seam through which it could be packed with filling until it was the shape and size I wanted. A bag of soft filling was also provided. The nurse asked how I was getting on with the exercises. Proudly I demonstrated the wall crawl. I'd managed to increase the distance I could move my left hand up the wall by a few centimetres, and she was pleased to see I was making progress albeit very slowly. A brief lecture on bras followed. I was told never to attempt to wear underwired bras again; instead I was to choose styles that were fairly high at the front, special mastectomy models that have a pocket into which a prosthesis can be slipped, holding it snugly in place. I was given a couple of brochures to take home, displaying attractive mastectomy swimwear including bikinis, as well as bras. The nurse gave me an appointment to see her in December for the fitting of my permanent breast form. Wishing me a good recovery she left, and I was alone with my softie.

Examining it, I thought that although it was an excellent idea for me to have one of these, it wasn't something I would want to use all the time. Before the mastectomy I'd decided that I would only put on a bra if for any reason I needed to wear smart clothes that warranted a full shape. I imagined that after this surgery the constriction of a bra would feel irritating for me. But I was happy to have the softie because it meant I had a choice. For outward appearances I could present myself to the world with a full bosom again if I wished, and this was the important thing.

Although this was the third day after the operation the loss of my breast still didn't in any way upset me, because I was just thankful to live. My sole thought was that the part of me posing the threat to my life had gone. We are not our bodies; we are the beings that inhabit them, and we women are far more than our breasts. They are of course a symbol of our femininity and an important part of our sexuality. The adoration of the female form, by both sexes, is absolutely natural and normal. A woman's body is beautiful after all, rounded and curving, soft, sensual, sexually inviting, stimulating, exciting, nourishing and satisfying. But women don't have to be built like a centrefold to be able to bestow all these gorgeous gifts of their femininity. Every woman posesses the power to be a goddess whether she has two, one or even no breasts, because her real beauty, the Spirit of the Divine Female, comes from within. I believe that the emphasis placed on the desirability of a perfectly formed bosom does nothing to make it any easier for breast-cancer patients to come to terms with their disease, their mastectomies or other forms of breast surgery. Many women might find it much easier to cope with losing one or even both breasts if less credibility was given to the idea that a fabulous cleavage is the be-all and end-all of female sexual attractiveness. I intended to continue living my life after the mastectomy as the essential woman I had always been. I may have lost a breast, but I am still able to give my man the smile that seduces him, or the touch that makes him tingle. *This* is my power, my womanhood. These things I shall never lose.

When I was in hospital a couple of the nurses asked me if I would consider joining the organisation 'Breast Cancer Care' as a volunteer helper. I'd already decided to do this before I had the mastectomy. Breast Cancer Care is an organisation offering support and advice to sufferers of breast cancer and their families. I'd read several of their fact sheets before the operation, and was so grateful for the advice they gave that I wanted to offer whatever help I could, once I'd fully recovered. Most of our misfortunes in life can invariably be turned into something positive, and what better way is there of doing this than to use our own experiences to help others? Fundraising is an activity open to anyone at any time, but there is even more that people who have had breast cancer can do. After two years have passed following the completion of all our treatment, we can undergo training that will enable us to talk to newly diagnosed women who are anxious or frightened, supporting them, offering comfort and reassurance that they too can both look and feel great after their surgery and treatment. There is also a scheme through which partners of breast cancer sufferers can train to talk to the husbands and partners of recently diagnosed patients. There are many worthwhile things that can be done by those who have been personally affected by breast cancer. It is so rewarding to be able to help other people try to deal positively with something that once threatened to destroy our own lives, and to know that much good can emerge from our personal suffering.

It is a very strange, awe-inspiring thing, that sufferers of cancer in any of its forms develop remarkable inner strength and immense courage. This can be an inspiration for others starting out on their own healing journey through cancer treatment. While I was in hospital I made up my mind that I would, at some point in the future, do all I could to try to help some of those whose destiny it is to endure what I had gone through. Somehow, this aim gave a kind of meaning and purpose to what had happened to me. I hoped that my cancer wouldn't pose any future threat to my life, so that I'd be able to achieve it. I was playing a waiting game, because I still had to be told of the findings from the tests on my tumour and lymph glands. Nothing was cut and dried. Nothing was certain.

When Pete arrived I showed him the softie and we talked about all the things that had taken place that morning. When I told him I wanted to join Breast Cancer Care as a volunteer helper he expressed doubts, concerned that I would become so immersed in the subject of breast cancer that it would take over my life. In no way did I intend this to happen, and I knew that in time I'd be able to show Pete that his fears were groundless. I was prepared to wait. This was easier than trying to convince him that I wouldn't do anything to exhaust myself, or becoming argumentative in defence of my aspirations. I understood my limitations, and also that however small my contribution might turn out to be, this work was something I was meant to do. But I fully understood Pete's concerns. I knew also that I might have much to go through before I could even think about the long-term future. But it was good to have some sort of a goal to aim for, and this helped me even more to maintain my positive outlook.

Later on my consultant came to inspect the drain, saying it could come out next day and I could then go home. This was wonderful news. Pete left in the early evening, leaving me to my thoughts and dreams of our future. I went to sleep that night feeling cheerful and composed, ready to pick up the threads of my life from where I'd left them four days ago. Tomorrow, Pete and I would be back home together, looking forward to getting on with our life. But it wouldn't be like it was before. Our life would never be the same again, we knew this, but what we didn't understand at that time was the degree in which my breast cancer was to affect it in the immediate future. Our most testing endurance was yet to come.

Twenty-One

I was so excited when I woke up next morning that I could hardly contain myself. It felt absolutely great knowing I would be home later, and that tomorrow I'd be able to go out and see all the people I knew once more. I was longing to show our friends that I felt fine after the mastectomy; that I was the same person I'd always been despite what had happened. I felt extremely well, and one of the nurses told me I looked radiant. I was ready to greet the world!

Pete arrived early, bringing a bag containing clothes for me to go home in. I'd been told not to get dressed until the drain had been taken out, and I was really impatient for this to be done. All I wanted now was to return to normality as soon as possible, to get on with living and put the mastectomy behind me.

When the nurse came to remove the drain she suggested Pete left the room, saying it wouldn't take long and that he could come back in a few minutes. I was glad when he went because I'd been told it might be uncomfortable when the tube was taken out, and I didn't want Pete to be there if it was going to be a painful process. The tube was held in place by two stitches, and to complicate matters my skin had healed tightly around it. I braced myself, not really knowing what to expect.

The nurse told me to relax as much as I could and try to think of my favourite place. I closed my eyes. The bed became soft grass, and before me lay the magnificent great trilithons of Stonehenge. Barefooted and with reverence I entered the temple between the massive portal stones, feeling the protective encirclement of the megaliths shielding me from all harm. "Where are you?" the nurse asked as she gently wiped the area round the tube's point of entry into my chest. When I told her she gasped, exclaiming "What a fabulous place to be!" I smiled, appreciating the empathy between us. She understood my choice of special place, because during the short time in which we'd got to know each other we'd discovered that our beliefs and philosophies of life were similar and that we had much in common. As she prepared to cut the first stitch she warned me that it might hurt a little. I said it was all right, asking her to just get on with it because all I wanted was to know the thing was out.

The stitches were easily removed but the tube was stuck fast because of the healing around it. The nurse said "I'm so sorry, I'm going to have to pull it now, and it may be a little painful for you." Her face was full of concern and she was clearly upset at knowing I might suffer some pain because of what she was about to do to me. But she needn't have worried, because by this time I was dancing, wild and unconstrained, in and out of the stone giants, thoroughly enjoying myself in the brilliance of the midsummer sunshine that illuminated my vision. The nurse pulled, I yelled, but it was more a cry of jubilation than of pain. The tube was out and I was free! I gave a huge sigh of relief as the nurse said, "Well done, Chrissie." She seemed as relieved as I was that the drain was out. It had left a small hole that bled a little, but the dressing she applied was firm enough to stem the flow. It was all over. Lightly I skipped out of the sacred space and back into my hospital room.

The nurse told me to avoid getting the dressing wet if possible, saying it should be left undisturbed for several days. The hole, although small, needed to heal over and it was important to keep it covered and dry. We hugged each other before she went away, and as she left the room Pete came back in. He asked if it had hurt when the drain came out. I said it was uncomfortable at the time, but not any more, which was the truth. Then, Pete bent his head and gently kissed the plaster covering the hole. I swivelled round on the bed to face him, and we held each other really closely for the first time since the morning of my operation. Feeling so free to move after that drain had gone was just wonderful, worth every second of the discomfort, which was only momentary and not really anything to be afraid of.

I'd been told I could go home after lunch but that a doctor would come to see me first, and by the time I was given the go-ahead to leave the hospital it was three o'clock. I'd dressed and packed my few things after the drain had been seen to, eaten lunch, and was impatient to get going. Pete made three trips to the car with all my flowers, which I wanted to take home. I had a final look around the room that for the past four days had been my home. I'd felt secure there, with staff on hand all the time to offer help and support if I needed it. Now, it was time for me to return to my own environment. Pete would be there, my rock to lean on, as he had always been. I realised how lucky I was to have my man beside me, and felt very sorry for single or widowed women who have to cope alone after their mastectomies, without a husband or partner to give them support. What courage and strength such women must possess, I thought, as I envisaged the help and support I knew I'd receive from Pete during the weeks ahead. I resolved to get back to normal as soon as possible, to stay cheerful and positive, to smile and be happy, so that Pete would feel encouraged and uplifted. He deserved nothing less than this. I wanted to do as much for myself as I could, although I knew Pete would willingly do anything for me. We'd both suffered this crisis, this emotional trauma. We needed to recover from it now, individually and as a couple.

Together we walked down the hospital corridor, Pete carrying my bag in one hand, his free arm protectively around my shoulders. Passing the nurses' desk we stopped to thank those on duty for all they had done for me, and for us. Thanks were also given to the girl who had brought my meals, and the porter who had taken me to the operating theatre and brought me a newspaper each day. He was clearly touched by the fact that his contribution to my welfare had been acknowledged and appreciated. Every single member of staff in a hospital, from the highest consultant to the volunteer helpers, deserves recognition for the valuable contribution they make towards the efficient working of the team as a whole. Each one is important in his or her sphere, and deserves to be shown gratitude. With the porter's cheerful "Take care of yourself Mrs. Rayner, good luck and thank you" ringing in our ears, we headed for the way out, extending final words of thanks to the receptionists at their station near the exit. Stepping outside I took several deep breaths of cool, fresh air. It felt marvellous to be out of doors. My legs were a little wobbly as I walked to the car. Pete opened the door for me and I got in. I couldn't wait to set off for home, but was dubious about wearing the seat belt because it passed directly over the site of my wound. Pete, resourceful as ever, placed a soft towel between the belt and my chest, to cushion it. We kissed, grinned at each other as he turned the ignition key, the engine responded and we drove out of the hospital car park. I was ecstatic. I was going home!

It felt strange and a little unreal to be back in our house after almost a week away. I've had several stays in hospitals in the past, and I always found that waking up on the morning after I came home was the best time, the time when I began to feel as if I'd never been away. Sometimes people become very anxious because of the feelings of insecurity they experience when they first come out of hospital, but this usually passes when normal life is resumed and they start to get out and about again. I knew my feelings of unreality would be short-lived.

Pete took my things upstairs after unloading the flowers, which I arranged in vases. The flowers filled the room, and I was deeply moved by the sight of them, beautiful reminders of people's love and caring. A heap of cards lay on the table waiting to be opened. I was very touched by the extent of the kindness that was being shown by so many people. As I started to open the first card I heard a knock at the door. It was our neighbour and very close friend Lyn. She had seen us come home and wanted to pop in for a few minutes. Lyn wore a wonderfully incredulous expression, and it did me good to see her so surprised by how well I looked. She said she was amazed to see me looking just like my usual self. This really pleased me because it was the reaction I'd hoped for. The last thing I wanted was to hear people say how sorry they were that I looked poorly, or that they thought I should be in bed, and so on. I think it was because I knew I had much to be thankful for, and nothing to cry about, that I looked so well and cheerful. Lyn left with a beaming smile on her face and I knew I'd scored some of the 'Brownie Points' I'd set my heart on winning.

Pete made us a cup of tea, and the spirit of normality gradually descended upon me as I sipped the warm, refreshing brew, savouring the old familiar taste. We were together again, and it felt fabulous. Pete cooked our dinner that evening and, shortly after we'd eaten, we went to bed. It was still early but we were both very tired, and besides, we needed to cuddle and hold each other. We'd been looking forward to this moment so much. It was lovely, lying in Pete's arms once again. I didn't care that it still felt a little strange to be home. The important thing was that I was with the man I love. I fell asleep in his arms, feeling contented and supremely happy. Tomorrow I would see our friends. I was ready to prove to everyone that there is, without any doubt, life after a mastectomy. The Amazon had lain down her bow, put aside her armour, and was ready to rejoin her people.

Twenty-Two

I lay awake as dawn broke, feeling safe in the environment of home. The light of the rising sun filled the room, and I sat up in bed so that the healing rays shone directly onto my face and chest. I closed my eyes, absorbing the glorious sensations of light, warmth and power. I hadn't realised just how much I'd missed the early morning sunshine until now. My hospital room had faced a different direction and received no direct sunlight until later in the day. Pete woke, and we enjoyed the sheer bliss of being together again. For four long days we had lived for this moment. As with all good things that are worth waiting for, it had arrived at last.

I wanted to go out as soon as possible after breakfast and felt very excited, craving to see everyone again. The town would be much quieter now that most of the bank holiday tourists had gone. There would be no pressing crowds. It would be a joy to walk out this morning. The locals would be doing their shopping, and I looked forward so much to seeing them all.

We were almost ready to go out when there came a knock on the door. Our close friend Robert had come to see Pete, thinking I was still in hospital. I will never forget the expression on Rob's face when he saw I was home. It was a mixture of surprise, shock, amazement, bewilderment, joy and relief. He was speechless. I greeted him with open arms. Enveloping me in his, Rob hugged me and sobbed relentlessly. My hair became saturated with his tears. I wasn't surprised by his reaction to seeing me for the first time since before my breast cancer had been diagnosed. Although it had gone against my better judgement, Rob was the one person I hadn't been able to bring myself to tell, and I'd asked Pete to gently break the news to him for me. I knew he would be devastated by it, but at that time I didn't think I could bear seeing him upset. Pete told him when I was in hospital. The news had shattered him, as I knew it would, and I was relieved to know he hadn't heard what had happened to me from anyone else. I stood quietly as Rob hugged me, deeply moved by his need to cry.

When his tears subsided we were able to talk. The three of us chatted away for almost two hours, and although this made me very tired it did me good to see our dear friend. Pete and I were both very pleased he'd called, because we really enjoyed his visit. Eventually I had to go to bed. I'd been told to have a lie down for an hour or so each day, until my full strength returned, and I was exhausted. It was only midday but I slept soundly for a couple of hours.

When I came round Pete and I had lunch. He'd prepared an amazing salad, which I really enjoyed. My heart was still set on going out, but after I'd eaten I realised that it would be too much of an effort, and instead we spent the rest of the day sitting in the garden, or doing little unimportant things around the house. I had another restful night, and in the morning I really was ready for that all-important first walk into town.

It is only a ten-minute walk from our house to the shops, but it took us twice as long because I still felt weak and couldn't walk at my usual speed. Eventually we reached the main street, and no sooner had we set foot in it than people we knew came rushing up to greet us. Everyone was clearly very pleased to see me out of hospital and us together again. This really touched a chord with us. It meant so much, seeing how interested folk were in hearing how I was doing, and receiving such support from everybody. We were absolutely amazed at the depth of everyone's kindness and concern.

We thought it would be nice to pop into our favourite teashop, and I sat at our usual table while Pete went to order at the counter. He returned looking very thoughtful. I asked if anything was wrong. "Stephen and George have paid for us to have tea and cakes when we come in here for the first time after you're out of hospital," he explained. I was bowled over by this kind-hearted gesture from two more of our closest friends. It is said that actions speak louder than words, and this act of friendship epitomised the proverbial phrase. We both enjoyed the little treat Stephen and George had arranged for us, appreciating the thoughtfulness behind it.

Walking home after that first trek into town since my mastectomy, I felt triumphant. I'd dealt with the shock, the fear, the doubts, the operation, and come through it all. I'd faced the fear, challenged and defeated it, treading it underfoot and grinding it into the dust, and had emerged from this experience a much stronger woman than I'd ever imagined I could be. Naturally I was apprehensive about my prognosis, but I was determined that however bad this might be I would handle it, using my recollections of the courage of those cancer patients with whom I'd come into contact since my own diagnosis as my inspiration. Every one I'd met exhibited such incredible bravery, optimism and sense of humour. Without exception they all exemplified what it is to have a positive attitude, not only towards their cancer but also towards life in general. Not one spoke of loss, suffering or despair, even those dear, brave souls whose prognosis wasn't good.

I didn't want to dwell on thoughts of the future in terms of my survival because for one thing I hadn't yet been told about the findings, and I knew it could well be that I had little, or nothing, to fear. I concentrated instead on the present, enjoying every moment of life. I was back in my community, ready to resume living, and I felt ten feet tall.

Everyone we met was very surprised to see me full of confidence and looking well. I enjoyed surprising them, giving positive messages to them all. Negativity only ruins whatever happiness there is to be had in living. Life is one of the two greatest gifts we can ever possess. The other is love. Without love, we cannot hope to get the best out of life, or to give our best to others. But the loving has to be unconditional, expecting and demanding nothing, given solely from the need to want to make other people feel cheerful and appreciated.

The ability to remain cheerful when confronted with difficulties is a great blessing, because not only does a cheery disposition facilitate our enjoyment of life, even though we may feel we have suffered extreme heartache or loss, it also helps to brighten the lives of other people. Optimism, smiles and laughter attract others to us, where complaining, dreariness and miserable faces drive them away. As far as we were concerned, Pete and I had every reason to be euphoric, and we certainly didn't intend to go around with misery and self-pity written all over our faces. The loss of my breast had opened the gateway to our future, enabling us to carry on living and loving. This was all that mattered to us. Nothing else was of any importance except our life and our love. I felt truly blessed to have both.

Lucy and Neal arrived in the evening. I was having a lie down in bed when they got here, and Lucy ran upstairs to see me. She was clearly upset at seeing a plaster where my breast once was. She found the whole thing extremely difficult to deal with, because she didn't want to accept the fact that I'd had cancer. I could see she was in denial, and I knew that this would only prolong the agony she was bound to go through when the full realisation hit her. There was nothing I, or anyone could do. Lucy would come to terms with it in her own time, when she was ready. I couldn't help feeling sorry for her, but we all have to discover that life holds unpleasant shocks in store, as well as the happier experiences. As we get older we learn to accept this, but for a young person, just starting out in life, it feels catastrophic when something like this happens, and it seems as if their entire world has been shattered. In time I knew Lucy would find it easier to accept the reality of what had happened, but I realised this could take months, maybe even years. It wasn't going to be easy for any of us, coping with what the future might hold, but as a family the three of us have always tried to pull together and I was determined that I would continue to be as brave as I could for all our sakes. My intuition told me I was going to be all right, and I placed all the faith I had in it, knowing it wouldn't let me down. I wanted Lucy to believe this too, but I was wrong to expect her to do so at this early stage. Everything was too uncertain as yet for her to feel anything but glad I was here in the present moment.

Neal came up to see me after Lucy had gone downstairs. He sat on the bed and gave me a gentle hug. As he did so, an impulsive thought entered my head. "Would you like to see my scar?" I asked, wondering if he would be shocked at me making such a suggestion. I needn't have worried. "Sure, if you want to show me." I pulled the dressing down to reveal what I could of the cut. "That's quite impressive" Neal said, grinning at me. I smiled back. He had realised I needed a reaction, and had given me the one I wanted to see. I was pleased with Neal's response, knowing I was right to feel I was no less a woman despite the loss of half my bosom.

Neal left, saying he would come to pick Lucy up at the weekend. It was good for the three of us to be together again as a family for a day or two. I needed to have Lucy near me, so that I could try to help her accept what had happened. But she didn't want to even think about it, no matter what I said or did, and I was content just to spend a couple of days enjoying her company.

By the weekend I was feeling stronger and less tired. I wanted to get on with looking after my house and us once more, to get back to normal. Lucy was a little upset about leaving, but she brightened when I told her I thought it was important for all of us to resume our normal lives and routines as soon as possible. I knew she would eventually gain strength from what had happened, and that this would be her mainstay when handling her own crises in life, as inevitably she would have to do in future time.

Twenty-Three

In the early days after leaving hospital I noticed that most people who knew about my mastectomy had one thing in common. This was a tendency to keep glancing down at my chest as we talked. I would be speaking face to face with someone, quite normally and casually, when all of a sudden his or her gaze would become firmly fixed on my bosom area! Instead of being able to maintain eye contact with people I often found myself addressing their eyelids, and after this had happened half a dozen times I decided to do something about it. I had no problem with folk wanting to look at me. My concern was that they shouldn't feel they had to do it surreptitiously. I understood their natural curiosity, and also the embarrassment some people obviously felt when they realised I'd seen them staring at my chest. I didn't want people to feel uncomfortable, so I began telling those whose curiosity clearly needed to be satisfied that I didn't mind if they wanted to have a proper look at my affected side, and I invited some to feel the flatness of my chest if they wished to go that far. With my hand guiding theirs, I held their palm over the place where my breast had been. Some may have thought it was a shameful or even disgraceful way for me to behave, (although I was never aware that anybody did) but if so this was their problem, not mine. This way of doing things, being frank, open and unembarrassed about what had happened, worked for me. It helped people lose that compulsive urge to keep trying to take a peep as we were talking, because I had dealt with this in a matter-of-fact, hopefully inoffensive kind of way. I didn't need to adopt this strategy in every case, only when speaking to people who I saw attempting to steal a look, trying to do so without my noticing but failing abysmally! I did it for them more than for myself, because I wanted everyone to feel at ease with me, just as they'd always done.

After the dressing had been dispensed with I showed some the scar as well. Few people have seen what a woman looks like after a mastectomy, and many of my friends were pleasantly surprised to see how natural everything looked. I think they'd expected to see a gaping wound, instead of the clean and tidy expanse of skin, neatly stitched, looking pink and healthy. I didn't object to showing anyone my scar if they were interested in seeing it. I was as proud of that scar as I would have been if it were a golden trophy. It was part of me, just as my breast had been, and I saw no reason to be ashamed or embarrassed about it.

It can be a terrible blow to a woman to lose her breast, and for many the experience is understandably devastating. I think that for such a woman, the realisation that people are looking at her chest in an attempt to see the flatness of it, or the difference in it, must be very upsetting. I believe that by taking charge of the situation, this gave me power instead of taking power away from me and making me feel as if I was a victim. I was in control of the mastectomy I'd had, it didn't control me, and I wouldn't settle for anything less.

On the third morning after I'd come home from hospital a most extraordinary and remarkable thing happened while I was lying awake in bed in the early hours. My eyes were closed and I was on my back. All of a sudden I felt a hand resting on my forehead. The touch, although gentle, was also quite firm. The warmth of that hand was penetrating and wonderfully soothing. I lay with my eyes still closed, enjoying the lovely feelings the touch of it was filling me with. After a minute or two I opened my eyes and turned towards Pete, to tell him how wonderful the touch of his hand was making me feel. But his back was towards me and he was sound asleep! I was shocked. The hand I'd felt had clearly not been his, and there was no doubt that I had felt a hand resting on my brow. Without waking him I laid on my back again, and no sooner had I closed my eyes than I felt not one but many hands stroking my chest and neck in caressing, sweeping movements from the direction of my bosom, up over my face and on towards the top of my head. I had the impression that three or four pairs of hands were involved, and I kept very still, not wanting the beautiful experience to end. This gentle stroking, with its accompanying sensations of peace, calm and loving care, continued for about thirty seconds before ceasing as suddenly as it had begun. I knew I hadn't dreamed it. I had been wide-awake, and it had actually happened. Then, the full realisation of what had undeniably taken place struck me. I had received a visitation, and been given spiritual healing. I will never forget that wonderful experience as long as I live. I whispered a prayer of heartfelt gratitude to whoever or whatever was watching over me, feeling so emotional that I began to cry. This woke Pete, who at once thought I was upset. I told him what I'd just experienced. When he realised that I hadn't imagined it, Pete was very moved. From that moment we knew everything was going to be all right, and that we had good reason to feel optimistic about our future. The healing hands had come to tell us all was well.

Twenty-Four

One week after my mastectomy the dressing had to be removed, and I was concerned about how Pete would react to seeing an eight-inch scar where my breast had been. He had repeatedly tried to reassure me that to him I would always be his beautiful woman, despite losing my breast. All the same, I was still worried. I needed to see Pete's reaction for myself before I could fully accept his assurances that he would be able to handle how I looked now. I couldn't help wondering if he might miss the sight of my breast so much that he would react badly to what he saw when I uncovered my wound.

I'd made up my mind that when I took the dressing off it would be an event, an experience we could both share. It was very important to me for us to make the occasion special. I hadn't had a bath since before the operation because I'd been told to keep the dressing dry for seven days. This was the eighth day, and I planned to take it off in the evening and get straight into the bath afterwards. The dressing over the hole where the drain tube had been had already fallen off, this had healed nicely and there was no need for me to worry about keeping it dry any more. I could hardly wait for the luxurious feeling of being submersed in warm, healing, scented water after having to manage with soap and a sponge for a week, and although I was nervous about Pete's reaction when he saw my scar, I was really looking forward to that bath!

In the evening I lit candles in the bathroom and filled the tub, adding a few drops of soothing aromatherapy oil to the water, along with some foaming gel. The sight of the bubbles and the scent of the oil was so inviting that I was tempted to jump straight in. But I still had to take the dressing off, and I wanted Pete to be there when I did so. I told him everything was ready. We pulled out the telephone plug so that we wouldn't be disturbed, and went into the bathroom together. At that time, Lucy was still at home with us. Earlier I'd told her what I planned to do, and when the time came she thoughtfully turned off the TV and went upstairs to her room, leaving us both alone together. Lucy realised how important this moment was for me, and understood the need for us to have no distractions.

I sat on the lid of the loo seat and Pete knelt in front of me. We kissed and held each other for a few moments. I was very tense. Pete sensed this, and assured me once again that I needn't worry about his reaction when he saw my body as it now was. Timidly I began to peel off the plaster. "No," Pete said softly, "I'd like to do that. May I?" His request touched me deeply and I was happy to let him.

Carefully and with extreme gentleness, Pete slowly eased the strapping around the edges of the pad from my skin, before lifting off the entire thing. I watched his face the whole time, waiting to see what was written there, knowing that this would reveal his true feelings. Without removing his gaze from my body Pete dropped the pad onto the floor. Tenderly he touched my scar, stroking it along its full length with his fingertips. He looked up into my face for an instant, before lowering his head to kiss the place where my breast had been. Long and lingeringly he kissed the scar from it's beginning in the middle of my chest, to where it came to an end beneath my armpit. I was in tears as I pressed his head closely to me. Then, Pete looked into my face, and his eyes were full of sincerity as he said, "Chris, you needn't worry. You look so beautiful to me at this moment, and you always will." He held me in his arms as I cried, and I believed him. I couldn't speak. All I needed was to be held. All Pete wanted to do was hold me. After a few minutes he hinted that I ought to get in the bath before the water became cold.

The feel of the water was fabulous. Pete got in the tub as well, sitting behind me so that I could lean back against him. I closed my eyes as he gently trickled the soothing water over my chest. This felt wonderful. The water was cleansing, calming and so relaxing. The candlelight flickered, bathing the small room in an ethereal glow. I knew Pete's words had been sincere. To him, nothing had changed, we were still the same people as before, and this was what mattered. His reaction gave me even more strength and confidence. From this moment I knew I really could go forward. There was nothing for me to fear. Deep down, I'd known all along that Pete wouldn't have any problem with how I looked now. But it had been so wonderful to experience his reaction, and to hear him say such consoling, comforting words to me at the time when I most needed them.

Later as we sat with Lucy in the firelight, I thought how blessed I was to be loved so deeply by my husband and daughter. I felt I had everything. My world was complete, and above all I was here to enjoy it. From this moment I intended to make the most of every minute of every day of the rest of my life. Life is too precious to waste it by worrying about things that really don't matter. The important thing is to live it to the full, making others happy too by being cheerful and fun to be with. Living is about using the life we have in good, positive ways rather than complaining or bemoaning our lot. It is about enjoying everything we have, and everything around us. Here, in the bosom of my little family, I glowed. My heart was full. Their love was without doubt my treasure on Earth, worth far more to me than anything. It was my richest blessing, because it gave me a determination to survive that was more powerful and commanding than anything I have ever known.

Twenty-Five

During the next fortnight I went to see the consultant a couple of times for routine post-operative checks. As always, Pete came with me. The consultant told us there was a possibility that I might need to have chemotherapy, but he wasn't able to confirm this until the results of the tests carried out on the tumours and lymph glands came through. On September 20th we went to see him again, to hear what those results were. It was a time of great uncertainty and apprehension for us. I felt uneasy as we sat in the waiting area of the breast clinic, wondering what lay in store for us now, hoping and praying that there would be nothing else for us to fear.

When a nurse called my name I felt sick and my legs turned to jelly. Pete held my hand as we followed her into the consulting room. I desperately needed to know how serious my cancer had been, and I had no time for small talk because the only thing that interested me was hearing the facts from the consultant. He sensed my agitation, and after asking how I was he came straight to the point. He had found a second tumour during the operation. Unknown to me, he told Pete about it before I came round from the anaesthetic. He said that in view of this, our decision to have the mastectomy had been very wise. The other, smaller tumour was growing behind the original one, closer to my chest wall. Pete hadn't said anything about this to me, because he thought it would be best if I heard it from the surgeon. I was shocked to hear that more than one tumour had been present, and so glad I'd opted for the mastectomy. The consultant went on to explain that other cells had been found to be undergoing changes that would probably lead to further malignancies in the future. Such is the nature of lobular breast cancer.

The good news was that the lymph glands were all clear. Five had been removed, none of which showed any sign of having been affected by the cancer. The margins of the tumours were also unaffected. Both features suggested that my cancer hadn't spread elsewhere, and had been confined to within my breast. This news came as a tremendous relief and my tension began to lift as I gradually took it all in. Then, the consultant said that because of the size of the tumours a course of chemotherapy was advisable. I had dreaded being told I'd have to have chemotherapy and, knowing very little about this treatment at that time, I was upset by the thought of it. The consultant explained that the treatment was intended to be preventative; that if any cancer cells were circulating in my body the chemotherapy would kill them. When most of us hear the word *chemotherapy* our first reaction is often to suppose the person receiving it has a poor prognosis. This was what I straightaway assumed, until I'd heard the consultant's explanation and been told that just because chemo was advised for me this did not imply that I was terminally ill. He went on to say that until a few years ago, chemotherapy would probably not have been prescribed for patients like me at all, because the tumours I'd had were of a size which at one time wasn't considered large enough to warrant treatment by this means. Guidelines had since changed, and nowadays chemotherapy is regarded as being the appropriate treatment in patients who, in years gone by, might only have been given radiotherapy. Nowadays, adjuvant therapy is frequently used to provide extra backup. (This is treatment that is given in addition to surgery, to reduce the likelihood of the cancer recurring or spreading). Cancer patients today are given the best possible care, which is why the rate of life expectancy is so much higher now than it used to be.

The dimensions of my tumours were 5cm and 2.5cm and were described as "extensive lobular carcinoma of the breast, stage 2." There are four recognised stages of breast cancer, ranging from least to most serious. Fortunately mine was at the less serious end of the scale. The consultant said that after the chemotherapy was completed I could expect to be given a course of radiotherapy to my chest wall. Again, this was purely for backup. I didn't mind the thought of having radiotherapy, it was the prospect of the chemo that really disturbed me, and the consultant understood this. He told us he had arranged an appointment for me to see the oncologist next, to hear the exact details of the treatment that had been formulated for me. (Oncology is the study and treatment of cancer.) I would be seen in the breast clinic again in a few weeks for my scar and arm movement to be re-checked, but now I had to go straight to the oncology department. The consultant pointed us in the right direction, wishing me well and saying he looked forward to seeing us both again soon.

As we headed for the oncology department all the old feelings of unreality came flooding back. Pete said he felt the same way. We were both taken aback to know I needed chemotherapy, and it was very difficult for us to absorb the news at that stage. We'd thought that once the mastectomy had been carried out, the cancer would be gone, and it would simply be a matter of my needing to have regular checkups and scans for a few years. Instead, we now had to deal with being told that I needed further cancer treatment, and treatment that we knew produces unpleasant side effects such as hair loss, fatigue and sickness. As always we tried to be cheerful. Pete said we couldn't change the fact that it had been recommended for me to have chemotherapy, and that he had faith in my ability to carry on being strong and positive. He said I must always remember he was there with me and would do all he could to make things as easy as possible for me.

I felt so upset for Pete, because here was yet another trial for us to endure. As we walked, I cast my mind back over the past twelve years, during which our life had been very difficult because my health had been extremely poor. I had continually picked up infections and was unable to shake them off because my white blood cell count was abnormally low. I'd been lethargic and tired much of the time. For many years I'd suffered from a long-standing generalised anxiety disorder, which didn't help, and to top it all a benign tumour was found to be growing in my pituitary gland, and this completely upset my hormonal balance and metabolism. When I was in my mid-thirties my body stopped producing oestrogen, although tests revealed that I definitely wasn't having an early menopause. The hormonal imbalances were so severe that I often became mentally and physically incapacitated, and because of all these problems I had to take early retirement from my teaching career. I relied on Pete for support because at times I was unable to shop, cook, clean the house or organise my life. At other times I would feel reasonably okay, but the bad spells gradually took over. I saw one doctor after another, all of whom prescribed similar drugs to try to shrink the pituitary tumour and restore my correct hormonal balance. Despite being treated with the type of medication that was considered appropriate for the pituitary abnormality, I felt increasingly worse as the years went by because the nature of my symptoms changed. I became a different person. I was obsessed with illogical and unsound thoughts and irrational fears that eventually took over my life. It was a terrible time, and things progressively went from bad to worse. Eventually, in 1995, I managed to see a specialist in London, who immediately identified what was responsible for my deterioration in health. He told me that the medication I'd been taking to control the pituitary tumour was, in his opinion, entirely unsuitable for people like myself with a long history of anxiety, and that the increased deterioration of my psychological well being was actually being caused by the drugs I'd been taking for so many years. What I was suffering from was their side effects! The specialist told us he'd heard identical stories from other patients in similar circumstances. His advice was to immediately discontinue the medication I was on at that time, and to wait for six weeks for it to clear from my system, before starting on an experimental course of hormone replacement therapy. A scan indicated that I was in the very early stages of developing osteoporosis, or brittle bone disease, and I needed oestrogen to improve my bone density. HRT had always been considered inadvisable for me because oestrogen is known to sometimes exacerbate pituitary tumours of the type I had, but fortunately in my case this didn't happen. Within a couple of weeks of coming off the tablets things started to improve, and gradually I changed back into the sound, level-headed person I used to be. My mind cleared, I was able to think and behave rationally again, and to organise my home and look after my family once more. When I started taking HRT my bone density improved and the oestrogen made me feel much better, both physically and mentally. Pete and I were able to enjoy our life again. Then, five years later, just as we were beginning to believe that all our troubles were over, the unthinkable had happened. This new crisis we faced, the development of my breast cancer, had the potential to be far more serious than anything in the past had ever been, and we'd thought nothing could ever be more devastating for us than that. I couldn't believe that Fate could be so cruel. But these things happen, and I knew we would both be strong enough to get through whatever lay ahead of us if we supported each other. Pete put a protective arm around me as we approached the entrance to the oncology unit. He knew how much I dreaded the chemotherapy.

Before we saw the oncologist a member of her team interviewed me. When this doctor asked about my previous medical history I looked straight at Pete. I'd suffered with such a diversity of complaints that it was difficult, if not impossible, for me to know where to begin, and thinking Pete would be able to explain things in a far more objective way than I could, I wanted him to start the ball rolling. He did so, and between the two of us we were able to describe all the medical problems that had plagued me since my mid-thirties. The doctor was very concerned about my low white cell count, because chemotherapy kills healthy blood cells as well as cancer cells, and it is the white blood cells that are responsible for fighting infection. There are several different types of white cells but it is those known as neutrophils that are of particular interest to oncologists during a person's chemotherapy treatment, although the other various types of blood cells, both white and red, are also kept a close eye on. Neutrophils are the 'expendable front-liners', for want of a better comparison, in the body's defence against invasion by bacteria or viruses. (I didn't regard any of mine as expendable, but valued each and every one. However few I retained during my treatment, *all* were precious.) They are the first white blood cells to surround any area of infection. Chemotherapy can severely deplete their numbers, and often a treatment has to be delayed to allow more time for them to be replenished. If a patient is given chemotherapy whilst his or her neutrophil count is very low, this can cause their immunity to be severely impaired, putting them at risk of serious infection. A low neutrophil count is known as neutropenia, and I had suffered with this condition for at least as many years as the other complaints I'd had. So it didn't surprise us when the doctor expressed some concern about my ability to tolerate chemotherapy. He leaned back in his chair, saying he had never come across a patient with such a complicated medical history as mine before, and that he thought it was no wonder we'd found everything so difficult to cope with over the years. The three of us laughed when Pete made the point that if anyone had to be different from the rest it was bound to be me!

The doctor said he would have to go and talk to the oncology consultant, to explain all this to her before she saw me, and we waited for about twenty minutes before he returned, saying we could go in to see her now. I started feeling shaky again. Pete put his arm around me, saying "Come on Chris, you can do this," and his words of encouragement made me feel braver. His support was just phenomenal, and to this day I don't know how he has managed to be so strong for me for such an incredible length of time. (I guess it must be love.)

The oncologist explained all that was to happen during my treatment, reaffirming what the breast consultant had told us regarding the size of the tumours in relation to the prescribing of chemotherapy. The regime planned for me consisted of a six-month course of CMF (Cyclophosphamide Methotrexate Fluorouracil) chemotherapy, followed by fifteen sessions of radiotherapy. I would also need to take the breast cancer preventative drug Tamoxifen for five years. I asked if I would lose my hair, and was told that the type of chemo I was going to be treated with doesn't always induce hair loss. Losing my hair would have been a very small price to pay for the peace of mind I'd gain from knowing I'd been given the best possible treatment, but it was something I would have needed to fully come to terms well in advance of it happening. The oncologist said that if sickness caused a problem, medication was available which would help to relieve this. It was impossible for her to tell us exactly how the chemotherapy would affect me because every patient responds to it in a different way. The other doctor had already told us that sixteen stone rugby players have been known to crumble under the side effects of it, whereas frail, little old ladies have sailed through their treatment with few problems. The tolerance level of each individual patient governs his or her reaction to this treatment. At this stage my ability to tolerate chemotherapy was an unknown quantity.

The thing I really wanted to know was the answer to the sixty-four thousand dollar question that was screaming in my head. "Am I going to survive?" Steeling myself and looking the consultant directly in the eye, I demanded a straight answer to it. Her reply was that the chemotherapy I was going to receive was being given for that very reason, to give me the best chance of survival. She told us that according to statistics the incidence of recurrence of breast cancer in patients with the same type as I'd had is higher without chemotherapy and radiotherapy, but that with it this figure is greatly reduced. The more treatment I had, the less likely it would be for my cancer to recur. When we heard this, Pete and I realised how important it was for me to have the chemo, and from that moment my attitude towards it changed. I no longer regarded it as something to dread or feel scared of. Instead, I began to welcome it, feeling very grateful for being given as good a chance as I could possibly have of survival. The oncologist said that if any cancer cells had managed to migrate elsewhere in my body, without this treatment they could begin to grow into tumours in other sites. Breast cancer is known to recur not only in the other breast but also in sites such as bone, liver and brain. If it does recur elsewhere in the body, it is known as secondary breast cancer. She made it very clear that I was strongly advised to have the chemotherapy. I agreed to it, there seemed no point in refusing to have treatment that is known to be effective in dealing with the potential threat that I faced.

The doctor went on to tell us that although I would have the chemo at this our local hospital, I would have to travel to Cambridge every day for the radiotherapy. We couldn't even think about this at that stage, it seemed too much to contemplate. Our main concern was with finding out all there was to know about my chemotherapy, and we asked for full details of how the treatment would be given, how long each session would take, how often I would need to go for treatment and so on. The answer was straightforward; the chemotherapy would be administered through a vein in the back of my hand. I would receive six cycles of treatment altogether, each one consisting of two consecutive weekly doses followed by a two-week recovery period. I would go for treatment on Thursdays, and each session would take about half an hour. Dose 1A would be given on the first Thursday, followed by dose 1B the Thursday after. Then I would have the next two Thursdays off, to enable my body and blood count to recover. One complete cycle of treatment therefore took a month. I'd receive twelve doses of chemotherapy altogether, over a six-month period. If my neutrophil count went too low at any time in between treatments, the next dose would have to be postponed until the count increased to a sufficient level to provide adequate immunity against infection. I was given several fact sheets about the type of chemotherapy I was to be treated with so that I could read about what to expect, and understand what was going to be happening to me.

The oncologist then turned to the subject of my history of neutropenia, saying she thought it would be advisable for me to see the haematology consultant before my chemotherapy began, to find out exactly what was going on with my white blood cell factory. The chemo was scheduled to start on October 12th, and I was told to expect to receive an appointment to see him in a few days' time.

In the car on our way home I was in a daze. I couldn't believe all this was happening to me. Pete said he felt certain that after I'd had all the treatment I would be fine, and told me I must try not to worry. He boosted my confidence with his unwavering optimism, and whenever any fears or concerns troubled me he was always able to reassure me and put my mind at rest. He reminded me of the pact we'd made on the day my diagnosis was confirmed, that we'd promised to confide in each other and talk about our fears together. When I asked Pete if he feared anything now, he smiled at me, saying he truly believed I was going to live to be a very old lady, and that I must never forget I was an Amazon. That did it! At once I felt brave and strong again, and during the next couple of weeks I prepared to face another battle, and to win the war. Because this, to my way of thinking, was what it was. A war against an invader of my body, and one in which the warrior had been given the direct order: "No Prisoners!"

Twenty-Six

The next day was the twenty-first after my mastectomy. I'd been told to wait three weeks before attempting to drive again, and now I wanted to give it a try. The mobility of my left arm was improving all the time, and I was looking forward to regaining my independence. It felt good to sit in the driving seat once more, but before I switched on the engine I went through the motions of changing gear, and applying the handbrake, because both of these actions had to be performed with my affected arm. Pulling the handbrake on felt quite painful, and I decided it would be foolish to attempt to drive anywhere until I could do this easily. It took only another couple of weeks before I found I was able to drive without any discomfort at all.

In the meantime I enjoyed going for walks, and later in the day Pete and I decided to gather some blackberries. It was one of those lovely, blustery, early autumn afternoons when, although the sun shone brightly, a chilly breeze was in the air. We enjoyed the trek to my favourite field, and finding the bramble hedges to be full of fruit we soon gathered enough berries for our needs. It felt good to be alive, to feel part of the living Earth. Stepping carefully over the low, outreaching branches of the bramble bushes I almost felt as if the land itself was greeting me, welcoming my return to it as I walked along, following closely behind Pete. After we'd gathered our berries we strolled home in the pale light of the fading sunshine, enjoying the togetherness that we value so much.

We made the most of this day together because tomorrow Pete was going back to work. He'd been at home with me since the day we were told I had breast cancer, and now it was time for him to return to his job. Although he said he felt fine about this, intuitively I knew he wasn't ready for it yet. But I didn't let on, knowing that if I said anything he would interpret this as my not wanting him to leave me, which wasn't quite the case. Even though I knew I'd miss him terribly I wasn't severely upset at the thought of Pete being back at work and away from me, but I had grave doubts about his ability to cope with the pressure and stress of it with me on his mind as well. I did all I could to try to make everything feel as though we were following our

93

normal routine. We had our evening meal early, I made the sandwiches for Pete to take to work, and we went to bed at a reasonable time. Throughout the evening Pete kept saying he felt okay about going back, and asking me if I was all right about it. I read the signals clearly.

Next morning just before he left the house, Pete came back upstairs to kiss me goodbye. Although he looked terrible, very tense and sporting a conspicuously forced smile, he said he felt fine and would look forward to seeing me when he got home at five that evening. I told him to drive carefully. I was very concerned as I listened to the car going down the road, hearing the noise of the engine getting fainter and fainter as Pete drove further and further away from me. I strained my ears to try to listen to it for as long as I could, until I heard it no more. Pete had gone, and I was alone for the first time since our troubles began. I decided to read the diary I'd been keeping since my breast cancer had been diagnosed. I wanted to remember all the things Pete and I had shared and done together during the past three weeks, thinking that by reading about us I would still feel as if he was near me. I glossed over the pages until I came to an entry recording one episode that had given me a terrible fright. A couple of days after I'd come out of hospital I'd had my breakfast in bed and was sitting there, blissfully thinking quiet thoughts, when out of the corner of my eye I caught a glimpse of a dark spot on my chest. Looking down, I saw a reddish-orange blob in the centre, right at the end of the scar. "I think my scar's bleeding!" I yelled, and Pete came charging into the bedroom looking frantic. "Where?" he demanded anxiously. "Here" I said, feeling queasy as I pointed to the globule. Pete prodded it with a fingertip. It wasn't blood at all. I'd had beans on toast for breakfast, and some of the sauce had dripped onto my chest! I had a good laugh at myself before closing the book and getting up.

I was on edge all morning, unable to relax because I had a strong feeling that something was wrong. Time passed slowly, and I felt certain that at any moment I would hear our car coming back up the road. I paced up and down, unable to focus my mind on anything but my husband, sensing that things were not as they should be and that he was in some sort of distress. The worst thing was being unable to do anything about it. I didn't phone him at work because I realised that if he had been finding things difficult it wouldn't help him to hear my voice. Eventually I sat down and waited. Just before eleven o'clock the phone rang. It was Pete on our mobile phone. He sounded very upset as he spoke. "I'll be there in ten minutes." He was on his way home.

When I heard our car pull into the driveway I rushed to the front door, waiting for the sound of Pete's key in the lock. When he opened the door I flung my arms around him. Tears were streaming down his face. He had completely broken down at work and his supervisor had sent him home. He'd been unable to cope with anything, and couldn't even bring himself to leave his office to go talk to his team because he was feeling so upset and insecure. I understood this, because without Pete near me I felt insecure too, incomplete, as though my dominant hand had fallen off. We stood in the hall hugging each other for a few moments, before going to sit on the sofa, all the while Pete apologising for "being so silly", trying to explain himself, saying it was stupid of him to feel this way. I had to force him to listen as I told him it was perfectly understandable for him to feel like this, and that I'd been expecting him to come home. I made us a cup of tea and phoned the doctor, making an appointment for Pete to see him that evening.

Pete was supposed to have gone back to see his doctor for a check-up on the day before he was due to start work again, but he hadn't done so, thinking he'd be all right once he got there. Unfortunately he was quite wrong about this. The doctor said that because of all the stress Pete was feeling it was too early for us to be apart, we were still dealing with something unknown, and this was why he couldn't concentrate on anything at work. Pete has never been one to go to the doctor for anything trivial, and often in the past I've had to force him into it, so the man knew this was serious and gave him another fortnight off, this time insisting Pete went back to see him before he attempted to return to his job.

During the next couple of days Pete picked up. He said he felt his 'job' at this time was to be with me, to look after me and be by my side. He needed to feel he was protecting me, saying he felt as if he was almost abandoning me when he left me that morning, and that he had to be with me as much for his own peace of mind as for his need to support me. The fact that I had a lot of treatment to go through had preyed on his mind so much that it was all he could think about. I told Pete I couldn't bear all this to be happening to him. He said he couldn't stand seeing it happening to me, that all I needed to do was tell him if I wanted anything, or anything done, and he would see to it. He told me he loved me and would do anything for me. He even said he wished he could have the chemo for me, to spare me going through it. If I was tired for a day or two after my treatments I wasn't to worry, but to leave everything to him. I knew then that Pete would probably be off work for a while yet. It hurt me to see the depth of his concern for me written all over his face, and I hated seeing him looking so anxious and troubled.

One morning I got up and found Pete at the kitchen sink, washing up from the night before. Putting my arms around him I whispered, "I'm glad you're here with me. Silly, isn't it?" "No it isn't silly," he replied, almost indignantly. "It's twenty-seven years of being together. It's the needing to care, and to deal with our troubles together like we've always done." His words "the needing to care" summed up our feelings for each other. The need to care for someone we really do love deeply becomes a driving force when that person is in trouble. When their love for us has been selfless and unconditional, we will do anything to try to help them feel better and make their life easier, because all we want is to see them well and happy again. I have always believed in unconditional love. If we are made to feel we are loved and appreciated only when we are doing what other people expect of us, or being what they want us to be, the magic doesn't work because it doesn't exist. There is nothing positive on which to build any permanent foundation of commitment when love is conditional. When we are loved and respected simply for being the people we are, nothing becomes too much trouble. This is how it has always been between the two of us. Nothing is ever expected; everything is freely and willingly given. Demands are never made, and appreciation is always shown. We have reaped rich rewards from our ability, and readiness, to put each other first. There is nothing that Pete and I wouldn't do for each other. I was going to be in a vulnerable situation in the immediate future, and Pete wanted to be there for me. This want became his need, and that was all there was to it. I would have felt exactly the same if the situation had been reversed.

During the course of the next few days the anxiety about seeing the haematology consultant built up in me, until a phone call came from his secretary, telling us we had an appointment to see him on 2nd October and that a bone-marrow sampling would be carried out then. Information had been posted to me, describing what to expect during the procedure. I didn't like knowing I had to have this done, but Pete put my mind at rest when he said the bone-marrow tests were probably just a precaution, and that I mustn't leap to the wrong conclusions. We'd both been advised to have 'flu' vaccinations prior to the start of my chemotherapy, and we had our jabs before I went to see the haematologist. My oncologist said this would be a good idea, because if I waited until the chemotherapy was underway the vaccination would be useless, as the treatment would render it ineffective. Pete was advised to have one as well because he works with a lot of people in an environment where infections spread easily and quickly, and we'd been told the worst thing I could get would be 'flu', given that my immunity, which was poor anyway, would be reduced even more whilst I was having chemotherapy. I felt so grateful for the care and attention I was receiving. Everything that could have been done for me and for us was done, and we both appreciated this more than words can ever say. The future was unpredictable, but the hospital staff did everything possible to ensure the present was as comfortable and secure for us as it could be.

We were absolutely exhausted by all that was going on, having to listen to, read and absorb so many facts, not knowing what to expect from the bone-marrow tests, the treatment I had yet to have and so on, and we needed a lot of sleep. Once, we were so tired that we went to bed at four in the afternoon, taking a picnic upstairs to eat when we felt like it, putting a "Do Not Disturb" notice on the front door and pulling out the phone plug! We needed all our energy and strength to help us put up with everything. I became more and more restless about going for the bone-marrow sampling, and by the time the day arrived I felt absolutely awful. But I knew this was something I had to do, for without it the correct dosage of chemotherapy could not be easily formulated, and my life could well depend on this. Once more we set off for the hospital, uncertain, apprehensive, but strong in our togetherness. This was just one more bridge for us to cross, and we told each other that in no time at all we would be over it.

Twenty-Seven

The test I was having done is known as 'Bone Marrow Aspiration and Biopsy' and is usually carried out in a hospital's haematology outpatient unit. The test analyses the status of blood cells in the bone marrow, and checks for the presence of any abnormal cells. The procedure takes about twenty minutes, but if a person opts to be sedated they are kept under observation for an hour or two afterwards until the sedative effect wears off. I'd been told that two samples of bone marrow would be taken from the back of my pelvis, although in some cases it can be taken from the breastbone. I asked if I would feel anything, and the haematologist told us that the drug used to sedate me wouldn't put me out completely, but would make me unable to remember anything at all about what happened. He said I'd be very drowsy and totally insensible regarding what was going on. I found this difficult to believe but after talking to the doctor for a while I began to feel less anxious and was ready to go through with the sampling. Then came the question "How long is it since you last ate and drank?" I said I'd had nothing since breakfast that morning. The resulting body blow knocked me flat. The doctor said I was supposed to have fasted since midnight! I had overlooked this instruction when I read the information leaflets that had been sent to me. I was devastated. I had got myself into a state of readiness, only to find I couldn't have the test because of my own oversight. I was really upset, because I knew I'd have to go through all the mental preparations again, and it seemed just too much to cope with. The doctor made arrangements for us to go back in two days' time, saying this was the earliest available appointment he could offer, and I promised him I would definitely not eat or drink anything after the appointed time on that occasion!

'Sod's Law' must have been written for us, because when we returned to the department on 4th October we were told that the consultant was off sick. I didn't know whether to collapse with disappointment or explode with frustration. His colleague came to speak to us, a pleasant female doctor who said she would carry out the sampling in his absence. At first I refused to go through with it. I had built up my trust and confidence in the other doctor and felt uneasy about someone else carrying out the procedure, even though common sense told me this lady would be just as capable of taking the samples as he was. I was given a while to think about things before deciding whether to proceed or to wait until the other doctor returned from sick leave, but nobody could say when that was likely to be. Pete said he thought I should just go ahead, because any further delay would only add to the amount of things I already had to think about, and I knew he was right. The doctor from the oncology team came to talk to me, saying I should proceed because the start of my chemotherapy didn't ought to be postponed. It was due to begin in eight days' time, and the oncologists needed the results of the bone marrow analysis well in advance so that they knew what dosage of chemo to give me. Everyone was clearly relieved when I declared that I was ready to continue as planned, and signed the consent form. Pete came with me as one of the haematology sisters showed me into a small side ward. I didn't have to undress, but was told to lie on the bed on my left side, and to pull my jeans down over my right hip. Pete sat on a chair next to the bed. I wanted him to be as near to me as he could get. He drew the chair so close that our faces were touching. The nurse gave me an injection in the back of my right hand, and that is all I can remember.

I came round to find myself tucked up in bed in a large, sunny ward. Pete was there, and I asked him what had happened when I was having the samples taken. He told me that the instrument the doctor used looked very much like a carpenter's gimlet. With one knee up on the bed, leaning all her weight on the instrument, she had pushed the point through my skin to the bone, and then screwed it in. Pete said this had really made him cringe, but the thought occurred to him that with his keen DIY skills, this was a job he could easily have done! He told me that when the doctor turned to pick up a syringe, he'd found it amusing, in a bizarre kind of way, to see me lying there with a stupefied grin on my face, completely unaware that I had a thing that looked like a woodworking tool sticking out of my hip! This made me laugh, I could just picture the scene, and I knew exactly what Pete meant. Then, he told me I'd rambled a lot while I was sedated. I asked him to elaborate, and when he did I was mortified! Evidently, I'd kept trying to recite that silly, fabricated book title, 'Bubbles in the Bath by Ivor Windybottom', and Pete said he had struggled to keep me quiet. Goodness knows where that one came from, although I do remember finding this extremely funny when I read it in a comic as a child. I was relieved to know I hadn't said anything worse.

A male nurse brought me some tea and sandwiches before I was given the all clear to go home. The drowsiness had worn off and I felt fine, apart from a little soreness where the surgical instrument had entered my hip. The spot was covered by a dressing, which I was told I could remove after a day or two. We were given a further appointment to see the haematology consultant in five days, when hopefully he would be back at work.

Returning on 9th October Pete and I were pleased to see the consultant, who had recovered from his brief illness. He was very glad that I'd gone through with the sampling because the test results showed that my bone marrow was definitely abnormal, and he said this possibly could have some bearing on my history of neutropenia. Although at the moment the abnormalities that had shown up weren't serious enough to give undue concern, the doctor thought it would be advisable for my bone-marrow to be tested again in the future. Without hesitation I asked him if this meant I was developing anything really serious such as leukaemia, and was relieved that the answer was a definite "No". But the doctor told us it wouldn't be advisable for me to have full-strength chemotherapy in view of the test results because this could completely knock out my white blood cell factory, leaving me without immunity to any infections I might come into contact with. Instead, he recommended an initial dosage of fifty percent, which would be increased gradually until my blood's optimum tolerance level was reached. My question then was that if my body couldn't tolerate full-strength chemotherapy, would this mean the treatment would be less effective in terms of the prevention of recurrence or spread? The doctor said that whatever level of chemo I could tolerate would in theory provide one hundred percent protection for me. This only temporarily put my mind at rest, because it was something that really worried me, and on 11th October when we went to see my oncologist prior to the start of my chemo the next day, I talked to her at length about it. She confirmed what the haematologist had said, and I began to believe it then. She also reminded me that there is a lower rate of recurrence of my type of breast cancer in patients who have had chemotherapy and radiotherapy, saying I'd have a much better prognosis with the treatment than without it, whatever the dose. I was convinced, and signed the paper giving my consent to have the chemotherapy. At one time I'd thought it might feel as though I was signing my life away, but now it felt as if I was signing an agreement to live. I was told to take great care not to come into any contact with bacterial infections, especially sore throats, because with my abnormal blood status there was a real risk that such infections would lead to serious problems. Fully informed, well armed with knowledge and information, I was ready to proceed with the chemotherapy, taking comfort in the thought that at this time tomorrow dose 1A would be all over.

Twenty-Eight

It is difficult for anyone to fully understand what chemotherapy is, what it does and how it affects the person receiving it unless they have been, or have lived with, a cancer patient undergoing this treatment. In simple terms, chemotherapy is a treatment using chemicals to kill cancer cells. It can be given intravenously, or by mouth in tablet form. When a higher dosage is required it can be administered slowly through a drip. Very rarely it can also be given in the spine. The action of chemotherapy affects healthy body cells as well as cancer cells, but whereas the normal cells recover and are replenished, the cancer cells do not, and they die. It is because of the effect chemotherapy has on the whole body that many people experience the harrowing side effects of hair loss, fatigue and weakness, nausea and sickness.

These side effects can be devastating, and I felt so ill during my treatment that there were weeks when it seemed as though I wasn't living at all, just merely existing. But this is *my* story, and it must be remembered that people react in different ways to chemotherapy. Some are able to manage their daily lives and even their work whilst being treated, whereas others may become so severely debilitated by the side effects that they find it impossible to do much at all.

Every treatment plan is personalised, tailored exactly to the needs of each individual patient. There are many different forms of chemotherapy, and a multiplicity of types of cancer. Chemotherapy varies from person to person according to factors such as the nature of the cancer they have, other medical conditions from which they might also be suffering, their general state of health, their blood status (as in my case) and so on. To the ordinary person in the street, chemotherapy is chemotherapy, namely 'a treatment given to cancer patients'. I found that very few of the people who stopped to ask me about mine knew anything more than this.

A patient's blood is routinely tested before their chemo is administered, usually on the day of their treatment. I'd had my test done on the previous day, after I'd seen the oncologist. My white count was high enough for me to have the first dose, and as Pete and

I walked through the doors of the oncology treatment area on 12th October I felt much stronger and more composed than I'd expected to be feeling. I knew how vital it was for me to have the chemo, realising that it wouldn't be in my best interests for me to feel nervous or anxious. The body reacts to stress, anxiety and fear by tensing up, and I wanted to be as relaxed as possible so that any discomfort I might feel when the needle was inserted would be minimal. I concentrated on breathing slowly and deeply as we waited for my name to be called.

Pete was invited to come into the treatment room with me, and it was reassuring for me to have him there. He sat on a small chair beside a larger armchair reserved for me. Two other female patients were in the room, having their treatments. Two chemotherapy sisters were present, really nice, friendly girls who instantly made us feel welcome and at ease. Nothing was as forbidding as I'd expected, the women having their treatments were chatting away to each other just as though they were in the hairdresser's or at a coffee morning, and each one was linked up to a drip. The atmosphere in the room was warm and comfortable. I felt calm, steady and all set to have my first dose.

Before I could have the chemo I had to place my right hand in a bowl of warm water. This, I was told, was to encourage the veins to 'come up' (become more prominent). After about three minutes I was able to sit down next to Pete. He held my left hand, speaking words of encouragement to me. I was determined to be brave, as much for his sake as for my own.

I had to have the chemo in my right hand because I'd had the surgery and lymph glands removed on my left side. After the mastectomy I'd been warned to avoid scratching or cutting my left hand or arm, because of the risk of infection with fewer lymph nodes there now, and all my subsequent blood tests and treatments were carried out using veins in my right hand or arm. One of the two nurses came to sit beside me. She examined my hand, spotted a suitable vein on the inner side of my wrist and gave my skin a wipe with antiseptic. I looked away, not wanting to watch the needle going in. Gently Pete touched my face, and I looked into his eyes, holding my gaze there until I heard the nurse say, "Well done, it's in," as she strapped the cannula firmly into place. A cannula is the appliance that is inserted into the vein, through which the chemicals are injected. Once in the vein they circulate around the body in the blood.

The three syringes containing my chemotherapy were in a tray, clearly labelled with my name and address, hospital number and other relevant details. Together the nurses checked the contents of the tray against my drug prescription sheet, to ensure that I was given the correct treatment. Checking was very thorough; one nurse called out what was written on the prescription sheet, the other confirmed that each of the syringes contained the corresponding, correct substance and dosage. Before the chemo was given I was offered tablets to combat sickness. (This type of medication is known as an anti-emetic). I asked what they were, and was told they were steroids. I said I didn't want to take them, preferring to try to manage without these drugs. I felt that enough potent substances were going to be circulating around my body, and wanted to keep any extra medication to a minimum, although most patients do take the steroids with no ill effects. The nurse then brought me a milder alternative to the steroids, which I didn't object to taking. I swallowed the tablet with a glass of lemon squash, kindly provided for me by a lady volunteer whose duty it was to fetch drinks for the patients from the hospital cafeteria. In addition to my cold drink she had brought us both a cup of tea. The kindness shown to us and to all the other patients was unbelievable. The devoted care and sympathetic attitude of the staff undeniably helped to make my treatment more bearable for us both.

Like the other patients in the room, my cannula was connected to a saline drip. The saline dilutes the chemotherapy, making it less concentrated. This is kinder to the veins, preventing them from hurting. The saline also helps to flush the chemicals around the body. After a few minutes the nurse sat down in front of me with my named tray on her lap. I stared at the three large syringes. The contents of two were colourless, but in the other the fluid was a clear yellow. The nurse picked up the first syringe, saying I might feel a brief sensation of coldness as the chemical passed into my vein. Pete gave my hand a reassuring squeeze. I watched as the nurse injected the contents of the syringe into the cannula. She was right about the coldness but the sensation only lasted a second or two. As the first syringe emptied she took the next, containing the 'Yellow Peril' as she jokingly referred to it, this time saying that I might feel a tickling in my nose, perhaps wanting to sneeze, but I didn't experience this at all. After the contents of the third syringe were injected I was very pleased with myself. I'd had dose 1A, and the countdown was now in progress. One down, eleven to go. It felt great!

Then the nurse gave me a pack containing boxes of tablets for me to take home. There were two different types of anti-sickness medication and some tablets marked 'Calcium Folinate'. I asked what this was for, and was told that this is what is known as a 'rescue' drug, used to help prevent mouth ulcers and soreness of the mouth that can sometimes be produced by the methotrexate. The drug 'rescues' the healthy cells in the mouth from being adversely affected. There were four tablets in the bottle, and these had to be taken at six-hourly intervals, commencing twenty-four hours after the chemo had been given. I was advised to take the anti-sickness tablets even if I felt I didn't need them. I was also given a small plastic ring-binder containing all sorts of information about my treatment, how best to cope with side-effects, details of what to do if I caught any infections, telephone numbers to call if I needed advice, charts for recording treatment dates, blood counts, temperature and so on. I was instructed to take my temperature regularly, to make sure I wasn't harbouring any infection. If it went above normal by even one degree I was to phone the haematology ward and go straight to the hospital, to be admitted for observation. All chemotherapy patients have to do this, it is a routine precaution, taken to ensure that if anyone does succumb to infection whilst their white blood count is low, they can be given strong antibiotics intravenously and kept in hospital until they recover. I was told in no uncertain terms that because of the state of my blood and bone marrow I ran a higher risk than usual, and needed to be extra vigilant. I had a card to carry with me wherever I went, marked 'Haematology Patient', giving details of the number to ring if I was taken ill at any time. I was determined to look after myself, to use common sense and avoid places where infections thrive, such as busy shops, cinemas, crowded pubs and so on. I didn't intend to become a hermit but at the same time I knew it made sense for me not to put myself in situations where the risk of picking anything up was a real one. The nurse agreed that this was the right attitude to have, and said that if I looked after myself as carefully as this I should be okay. She booked an appointment for me to have dose 1B the following Thursday, and Pete and I left the treatment room.

On our way out I noticed a woman in the waiting area with a pretty scarf tied around her head, and I knew she had lost her hair. We smiled at each other. I went to talk to her, and to the other people waiting for their treatment. It was as though we were one family, all united through our cancers and our chemotherapy. Pete and I spoke to everyone there, and some said we would be seeing them again because their treatment dates coincided with mine. In a way it was comforting to know that when we went for my chemo in the future we'd see people we recognised. Somehow this gave an impression of stability, even normality. We were far from alone. Thousands of people have chemotherapy every day, because cancer is such a prevalent disease in our society. Nowadays it isn't unusual to come across people who have either had chemotherapy, or who are currently having it, or have been told they are to have it in the near future following a recent cancer diagnosis. Or to meet individuals whose relatives or friends have been through this treatment. I realised, as I spoke to the other patients I met that day, that things could have been much worse for me, and that I was indeed fortunate to have a reasonably good prognosis. I told Pete that I felt full of optimism and hope, because I was being given all this treatment to enable me to live. Now, my sights were fully focused on coming back for next week's dose, because after I'd had it I would have completed one sixth of my treatment. All I had to do was to get through the next seven days.

Twenty-Nine

Throughout the following week I felt fine, with no obvious signs of any side effects. I was over the moon about this, thinking that the treatment would be easier to tolerate than my bone marrow tests had suggested, feeling hopeful that I would eventually be able to have my dosage increased to full-strength. Unfortunately I was wrong on both counts. On 19th September I had dose 1B at seventy percent strength, and from the very next day the side effects began to kick in. I felt as if I had a bad attack of 'flu'. My limbs and joints ached and I was extremely tired. Nausea and feelings of sickness came on during the second day, and lasted for over a week. The anti-sickness pills relieved this to a degree, but not completely, although they did make a tremendous difference and I could never have managed without them. I'd been given a fresh pack of tablets, even though I still had plenty left over from the previous week. The boxes of pills were stacked up at one end of our kitchen worktop, which soon began to resemble the counter of a chemist's shop. I felt so under the weather that I spent most of the first week after 1B sleeping in an armchair.

Gradually I became aware that I could taste the chemotherapy. The sensation was only slight at first, but it was unmistakably there. A friend, who'd recently had chemo herself, recommended ginger ale for the nausea, and Pete bought me a couple of bottles. This remedy worked quite well for me, and each time the sick feeling became really unpleasant I swallowed my tablets with a large glass of the fizzy drink. During the course of my treatment I tried ginger in several different forms; crystallised, chocolate-covered, biscuits, cake, ginger tea and wine, finding the chocolate-covered variety to be the most effective in reducing the feelings of sickness. (Besides, the chocolate was very nice too!) I must have consumed pounds of the stuff during that seven months, and it was no wonder that I put on quite a bit of extra weight, but the important thing was that it did the trick. The feeling of sickness was quite horrible, and not what I'd expected. It was like travel sickness, reminding me of when I used to feel ill during journeys in those old-style coaches or leather-upholstered cars when I was a child in the fifties. I was never actually physically sick but felt as though I was going to be, much of the time. It wasn't pleasant but, as with all things, it could have been worse, and at least the feeling eased whenever I ate. I was incredibly hungry all the time. At first I was concerned about the weight that seemed to be piling on, but after a while I gave up worrying about it because I needed to eat to make myself feel better. I ate little and often, which was what the chemotherapy nurses had advised.

Shortly after the start of my chemo, bright yellow envelopes began arriving in the post. These contained letters from John, my uncle. John and I have corresponded regularly since the 1970's, and we have grown extremely close over the years. I didn't tell him anything about my breast cancer before the mastectomy, but on the day after the operation I wrote to him from hospital. A few years ago John was taken ill, and at one point he was in hospital himself in a life-threatening situation. He didn't write or phone to tell us anything about it until he'd recovered and was back home. So I decided to do likewise, to show John that I'd inherited his same fighting spirit. The news had shocked and disturbed him, but he appreciated the reason for my delay in telling him, genially accepting the appropriate and well-deserved dose of his own medicine!

The first thing John did when he received my letter was to phone us. I will never forget his first words to me: "You've upstaged me haven't you, you naughty girl!" He told us that while I was in hospital he'd been on holiday, and that one night he had a compelling urge to phone us, for no particular reason other than he felt he should. When he rang, there was no answer at our end. The explanation for this was simple; at the exact time John phoned I was being wheeled off to the operating theatre!

Another odd coincidence concerned his yellow envelopes. They started arriving just as I'd begun to feel I needed the colour yellow in my environment. Yellow is a healing colour. It inspires cheerfulness and is uplifting. I'd suggested to Pete that we ought to redecorate our home in shades of yellow and gold, and he'd agreed this was a great idea. Lo and behold, in the letter John sent in that first yellow envelope he wrote that he'd bought a large supply of them, especially to use when writing to me throughout the period of my chemotherapy treatment! I was amazed by this, it was almost as though John had read my mind, and each week I looked forward so very much to the arrival of a sunny envelope through the letterbox.

The letters they contained were unparalleled. John wrote such inspiring, fortifying and comforting words, not only to me but to Pete also. The tone of his language often resembled that of a General addressing his troops on the eve of battle. It motivated me even more to keep up my courage, reinforcing my strength of will and purpose. John's words "This is OUR fight, and together we WILL win it!" used to move me to tears. He repeated this phrase so often that it had the subliminal effect of bolstering my will to win, which was clearly his intention. I felt he was with us all the time, despite the geographical distance between us. Never have we been offered such heartening and inspirational words of cheer as those written by my dear uncle during my cancer treatment. He appeared to have a clear understanding of our situation, and because of this I was able to express all my feelings to him when I wrote back. This was therapeutic, and of great benefit to me. Through the power of the written word I was able to discuss, with John, every aspect of my treatment and how it affected me. I expressed my feelings of despair and frustration during those frequent periods when I was unable to do anything except sit in a chair. I confided my worst fears, when the mental reminder that I was being treated for a life-threatening disease reared its ugly head. I unloaded my repressed anger concerning unresolved issues from my past. Any negative feelings or concerns that troubled me were discussed and resolved with the help, advice, and depth of understanding I received from John, and writing to him at this time in my life proved to be my long overdue and much needed catharsis. It is good for anyone to be able to unload all the useless emotional baggage they have carried on their shoulders throughout their lives, but especially so for cancer patients. Stress, anxiety, worry, emotional upsets and all the other negative things people are inclined to pick up along life's way are things we are strongly advised to avoid, and through my weekly correspondence with John I was able to release every single piece of my own polluting, rotten garbage, clearing the way for the absorption into my consciousness of bright, new, constructive and positive things. Things that will be far more beneficial to me in terms of my future health and well being.

With John I also shared my feelings of hope, joy and optimism, either when I began to feel better during the recovery period between treatments, or when each dose had been successfully completed. I wanted to tell him about the positive things too, and at one point, when I was almost through with the chemo and feeling the worst I'd ever felt, I wrote "I WILL return to normality and there I will stay, have no doubts." I wanted John to believe, as surely as I did, that I would be all right. I don't think there was one single, human emotion that wasn't touched on in our letters to each other during those long months. Besides his being my uncle, I came to regard John as my confidant, advisor and counsellor at that difficult time in my life when I really needed someone with sensitivity and understanding to talk to, rather than unload it all onto Pete, who had enough to think about in trying to cope from day to day with his concerns for me.

It was so beneficial for us to have someone close to discuss our feelings with during my treatment. My sister Liz also shared our joys and sorrows. Her support was constant; she phoned us every week, sometimes twice, and always after I'd had my chemotherapy. Just knowing she was thinking about me, and about Pete too, meant so much to us both.

Chemotherapy treatment isn't something that can simply be ignored or put to the back of one's mind, because the fact of the matter is it governs one's life. An hour or two spent in the oncology department of any hospital, talking to people who are trying desperately hard to bear it, would be enough to convince anyone that this treatment isn't something a person can just happily forget about after they have been given their dose. Chemotherapy tears a whole year or more out of people's lives, given the length of the treatment period and the time needed to get back to normal afterwards, which in itself can take several months. Chemotherapy *becomes* a person's life, there is no other treatment like it and people who have never had it cannot even begin to imagine what it is like. Pete and I found it impossible to plan or organise anything whilst I was having chemo, because everything we did depended on how well I was feeling. We would decide to go shopping, or out for a drive, only to then find we had to stay at home because I felt too sick, tired or ill to go. Just living and coping with the treatment and its side effects was the most we could do, and at times this was so very, very hard.

The side effects of chemotherapy can be severe and disabling while they last, but the important thing to remember is that they do go off eventually. For us, the time passed slowly, the months dragged on, our entire focus being on getting the next cycle over and done with. My treatment period was one of the most harrowing, unpleasant, demoralising and horrible times we have ever known. I was beset by many extra problems, which did nothing to make our lives any easier. These troubles began after my second complete cycle of treatment, when I started to experience profuse sweating all over my body, which was particularly bad at night. The sweats were accompanied by unpleasant sensations of extreme body heat, followed by freezing cold chills and tremors. The chemo had brought on menopausal symptoms, which really hit me hard and made life even more difficult. We had to sleep in separate beds because I suffered with insomnia due to the sweats. We didn't like this arrangement but neither of us could sleep if we were together, and it was our only way round the problem. Pete was still off work, but due to return in a few days, and we knew we'd have to sleep apart then because otherwise my insomnia and restlessness would disturb him too much. So we got into the 'separate bedrooms' routine well in advance, which was a good idea because at least it enabled each of us to get a reasonable night's sleep.

During my recovery periods I still needed to have regular blood tests. The samples were taken at my GP's surgery and then sent to the hospital pathology lab for testing. My neutrophil count was always low, frequently around 1.5. (On my blood forms the normal range was indicated as being between 1.8 and 7.7, these figures referring to the number of neutrophils per measured unit of blood.) Whenever they were really low, between 0.5 and 0.8, I worried about picking up infections and felt very vulnerable. Sometimes the anxiety was almost unbearable, and then I became upset and tearful, thinking this might mean I wouldn't be able to withstand the treatment after all. I knew that the chemotherapy offered the most likely assurance that Pete and I would still have many years of life to enjoy together. This was the one thought I clung on to, and I placed all my hope in it.

My treatment had to be postponed a few times because my neutrophil count was very low, and it would have been too risky for me to have the chemo. After travelling the almost thirty miles to hospital we'd go directly to Pathology for my blood test, I would be all keyed-up to have my chemo later on, only to then be told that the tests showed my blood wasn't up to it and we would have to wait a further week. For chemotherapy patients this is one of the most demoralising things that can happen. The disappointment is indescribable because the thing everybody longs for is to come to the end of their treatment, so that they can start recuperating from the unpleasant side effects that have been part of their lives for so long. I hated the constant weakness, and feeling generally unlike my normal self. It was disconcerting, and made me feel threatened. No matter how much strength a person has, chemotherapy can easily undermine it. But although my physical strength deteriorated rapidly as the treatment progressed, I retained my mental stamina, only giving way to tears on occasions when everything seemed too much to bear and got on top of me, which wasn't that often. At times it was good to cry, and the chemotherapy nurses told me it could only be beneficial to let it all out and have a sob sometimes, saying that people have to do this to help them release all the emotion. I realised that it was far better for me to have a good cry than to suppress my feelings, and always felt much better afterwards! I was sensible, resting whenever I felt exhausted, not even attempting to do anything when I felt ill because I found that any physical effort I made at those times rapidly used up what little energy I had in reserve. Too weak to even read books and watch TV for long, I slept and generally laid low for most of the time. As the treatment progressed I became weaker and weaker, with an awful pallor that I used to describe as "grey with yellow overtones." I invented my own little word to describe how I felt on bad days, which was 'chemoid'.

Nobody saw me when I was at my worst because I didn't have enough energy to even walk down the road, let alone into town. Whenever I did go out it was always when I'd recuperated, and of course then I looked pretty well, with a better colour and more energy. Only on one occasion did I force myself to go to the shops during a rough spell. A good friend's birthday was due and I wanted to choose her card myself. No sooner had I set foot in the street than a woman I know came up to me saying, "Get yourself home right now, you look absolutely dreadful." She wasn't being unkind, far from it, she was very worried by how I looked, asking me if I'd be all right going home by myself, and I really appreciated her concern. I knew I'd made a mistake by struggling to go out, selected the first suitable card I saw and dragged myself home. I felt so weak that I went straight to bed and stayed there for the rest of that day.

The chemotherapy affected me as badly as this because for a large part of my life I've had a weak physical constitution, with a very poor tolerance of illness. Not everyone feels incapacitated by it to such a degree, although many are affected in similar ways. Each of us has our own strengths and weaknesses. Just as one might be mentally strong where another may possess more physical energy, so everyone differs in the way they react to chemotherapy. But this treatment has to be borne, and despite my anxiety at the onset, when I got further into it I found my familiarity with how it affected me enabled me to cope. I soon discovered I was able to predict when to expect to feel rough, knowing I'd be foolish to attempt to do anything but rest at those times. Just before the halfway point the routine began to feel more usual, and I was able to accept it as normal. At first it felt so alien, to both of us, but as we became more accustomed to it our life settled down into the pattern, and we felt stable again.

Feeling ill and having to spend so much time at home was tedious and frustrating. I put on over a stone and a half in weight, not only because I wasn't very active but also because I couldn't ignore the gnawing hunger. Every week Pete used to buy me the chocolate ginger that helped to relieve my nausea, and on one occasion I scoffed an entire bag full in a day! It was self-indulgence like this that kept me going, little treats like chocolates made all the difference and gave me something to look forward to. As a rule I hardly ever touch the stuff, being a firm believer in healthy eating and preferring fresh fruit as a snack. I did eat lots of fruit as well, especially grapes, which helped to quench my thirst. I'd been told to drink as much water every day as I could, to help flush the chemo through my body. I drank litres of iced, bottled water, which I also found to be helpful in relieving the nausea. It was simply a matter of consuming what I fancied, when I fancied it, and not worrying about putting on the weight. I knew that once my treatment was over I'd be able to shed those extra pounds. Having this in mind gave me a goal, something to aim for. I enjoyed the thought of becoming active again, going for long walks with our dog through the woods that I love so much, cycling through the nearby country lanes, exercising and going to the gym again. It all lay ahead of me and I held onto the knowledge that this phase of my life, this ordeal I was going through, would one day be just a memory. But a memory about which, when I looked back on it, I would hopefully be able to proudly say, "I did that."

Thirty

At the end of November, Pete and I celebrated the fact that I'd successfully completed two cycles of chemotherapy, because this meant I was a third of the way through the course. This was the first major milestone we'd set our sights on, and to have reached it felt like a real achievement. Now, there were only four cycles to get through, instead of the six that faced us at first, and this really encouraged us. Pete was able to take days from his annual leave so that he could come with me when I went for my chemo, or stay at home on my bad days. Everything seemed to be working out well.

We spent a lot of time talking about our feelings together, and we both agreed that the positive side of the experience was that we'd learned a great deal that might be useful in helping others in the future. It was heart-warming to think that other people might benefit from the trauma we had gone through as the result of my breast cancer. I thought that if this was to be the case, then maybe the ordeal had a purpose. I didn't question anything, just accepted it as destiny, in which I strongly believe.

When Pete was at work I kept busy, always focusing my mind on positive things and making sure I had plenty to think about besides the chemotherapy. At those times when I wasn't able to do much because of the after-effects of my treatment, I used to spend hours reflecting on my life in general. Once, I cast my mind back to my early teens, remembering my first bra. I'd saved my pocket money and bought it in Woolworth's for the princely sum of half a crown, or twenty-five pence in today's currency. Size 32A, white, with a pattern of pink rosebuds, brand name 'Winfield'. Most of the other girls in my form at school wore them and I wanted one, even though I had very little to put in a bra at that time! But I was determined I'd have one so that I could feel as grown up as I thought all the others looked in theirs. Before I got mine I used to look at the outline of my friends' bras through their white school shirts and feel deeply jealous, wishing I could be like them. That first bra is so special, a tremendous esteem booster and confidence builder for many a pubescent girl, a visible symbol of her developing sexual maturity. I was so proud when my breasts grew, and as I remembered the insecure, anxiety-ridden young girl that I once was, I thought how fortunate it is that we aren't able to see into the future, or to know what Fate has in store for us.

I went for chemo 3A on 12th December, but because my neutrophil count was only 0.9 the treatment was deferred until the 28th. I was pleased about this because the last thing I wanted was to feel ill at Christmas, but I wondered if the postponement would be detrimental to me in any way. The oncologist said it was acceptable to put off an A dose, but not a B, because of the disruption to the cumulative effect of the two combined. If a B dose couldn't be given for any reason, the A would have to be repeated. I hoped this would never happen to me. I was feeling pretty good at this time, I'd had my recovery period from cycle two, and during the days leading up to Christmas I felt better and better, clearly because the existing level of chemo in my body hadn't yet been augmented by 3A. I went shopping for Christmas presents as if there was no tomorrow, loving every minute of it. I wanted this Christmas to be an extra special one, and I told Pete, Lucy and Neal that the reason for so many extra parcels under the tree this year was to celebrate the fact that my cancer was being treated and my prognosis was good. We had so much to be thankful for, and this year I really wanted to spoil everyone at Christmas!

The fact that I'd had breast cancer and was being treated with chemotherapy hit Lucy very hard. Whenever we spoke on the phone she was evasive, talking about every subject but the one I really wanted her to mention. Clearly she was still in denial, and this upset me because my daughter and I have always been able to talk about most things. She'd been raised with open-mindedness, and the natural questions all children ask (which for some people cause acute embarrassment) had always been answered immediately and truthfully, wherever we were or whoever happened to be present at the time. I never wanted Lucy to grow up with the notion that anything natural, such as bodily functions, sex and death, were taboo subjects. Not knowing what to think, I spoke to Pete about Lucy's reticence. I was hurting because she was avoiding the subject and I wanted to know what Pete thought about this. He said he realised from the outset that Lucy would find it difficult to cope with my breast cancer, and wasn't at all surprised by her reaction. Then, the realisation dawned on me. Lucy was frightened for me. By avoiding talking about it she was still pretending it didn't exist. Immediately I grabbed a pen and wrote her a long letter.

I explained to Lucy that I needed to know she was thinking about me when I was having my treatment. (I knew she was, but I just wanted to hear her say it). I told her that my greatest need at this time was in many ways similar to that of someone who has suffered bereavement, in that I should be allowed to talk about what I was going through, rather than have to endure the extra emotional stress of having this fundamental need denied. I emphasised the fact that the chemotherapy was providing me, and all of us, with a future we could look forward to, and that I longed for her to talk to me about my breast cancer, especially after I'd had each dose of treatment. I told her that both her dad and I needed her to be strong and supportive, rather than hiding her head in the sand, not because we wanted her to feel sorry for us, but because we loved her and wanted to reassure her that all was going well for me so that she wouldn't worry, that despite how ill I felt at times or how dreadful I looked when she came to see me, when I recovered I felt good. I wanted to share the encouraging things with Lucy, not the rest of it, and when I re-read my letter I was pleased with the way I'd worded it, hopeful that it would have the desired effect.

The phone rang early next morning while I was out with the dog. It was Lucy. She had received my letter. Pete said she was in tears, thoroughly upset because she hadn't realised how I'd been affected by her reluctance to talk to me. She'd promised to phone again so that she could speak to me, but I couldn't wait, and rang her straight back. We'd scarcely said "hello" to each other before she was upset again, but we talked the issues through and this did us both good. I will never forget the things Lucy said to me during that tear-jerking conversation: "I love you so very much Mum, and I don't want to lose you. Breast cancer is something that happens to other people's mums, not to mine. I can't bear the thought of you losing your breast, and now having to put up with this treatment, it's more than I can stand." Then it was my turn to cry. But after a while we were able to talk to each other without giving way to tears. Through our exchange of feelings Lucy understood how she could best support me through my treatment, and I understood that her previous inability to do so was solely down to her love for me as her mother, and her fear that I might not survive.

From that point Lucy was able to listen when I told her how things were progressing. I felt much better, knowing the subject had been aired and was now out in the open, no longer a forbidden topic as far as she was concerned. She still clearly felt uncomfortable about discussing things in too much depth, so I kept the details to a bare minimum, generally outlining the things I wanted her to know in a matter-of-fact kind of way. The main thing was that Lucy had started to accept what had happened, and even though it was still early days, I knew she had taken that first difficult step towards coming to terms with it all eventually.

When people shun difficult issues this is a reflection of their own insecurities and fears. After my chat with Lucy I understood completely why she hadn't been able to discuss my cancer treatment with me. Being young, the thought of her mum having chemotherapy was terrifying for her. But as regards a small number of other people who seemed unable, or unwilling to even mention what was happening to me and to us, I would much rather they had asked me if I wanted to talk about my cancer treatment than assume I didn't, or avoid the issue completely because they weren't able or brave enough to cope with the thought of it, or didn't know what to say to me. Whenever I was given the impression that what I was trying so hard to endure was being ignored, this both hurt and infuriated me. In situations like the one I was in, it is usually much better for someone who doesn't quite know what to say to admit to the fact, because this is nothing to be ashamed of. I needed good listeners, and it didn't matter to me if people knew what to say to me or not, as long as they were willing to allow me to express my feelings without fear of them dodging around the issue or swiftly changing the subject. I found the best listeners were those who had gone through similar experiences themselves. My advice to anyone with a friend or relative suffering from cancer and going through treatment is to ask them if they want or need to talk about it, and if they do, to give them your attention and listen. It makes a world of difference when we know people appreciate that we're having a hard time, and show an interest instead of behaving as though everything is normal. Things are never normal when someone is trying to get through chemotherapy, either for that person or their partner. We feel bad enough without having to put up with any extra tension, frustration or irritation. Speaking to other cancer patients I found that this was the view held by the majority. Of course, there will always be some folk who prefer not to discuss their cancer or treatment with anyone else, and their viewpoint should always be respected. But I am a great believer in talking about our feelings. This was a vital part of the healing process for Pete as well as for me. Which is why it was so good that we spent a lot of time talking to each other, because this helped us to get things like anger and frustration out of our systems.

Communication between people is so important, especially where relationships are concerned. However difficult or sensitive a subject may be for some people to talk about, more often than not it is beneficial for all concerned if they can bring themselves to discuss it. Honesty, openness and frankness can be used to pave a way to full understanding and acceptance of any situation, if people are willing to make use of these qualities. Hearts can be broken, lives shattered, and breakdowns in health may even be triggered if we refuse either to accept reality, to talk unashamedly about our innermost feelings, or to show willingness to allow someone else to talk about theirs. At this time in my life I was so thankful that as a family, Pete, Lucy and I have always been aware of the importance of keeping the line of communication between us open. Now, we were all reaping the rewards of this philosophy.

Thirty-One

On 19th December I went to see the breast care nurse to have my permanent breast form fitted. I was very excited about this and had been looking forward to it. My excitement mounted during the journey to the hospital, and when we got there I asked Pete to go on into town while I went for the fitting, which I knew would take a while. We arranged where to meet in town and Pete drove away. Today was also his birthday and I didn't want him to see how I looked in a bra because I had made certain plans for later!

I had taken three mastectomy bras with me that I'd purchased after looking at a brochure the nurse gave me when I was in hospital. They were all pretty and feminine, each having a pocket into which the breast form could be slipped, giving confidence that it would remain firmly in place. The nurse inspected and approved of my selection, saying I'd made an excellent choice. We got on very well together; our conversation was relaxed and full of laughter. Everything seemed so natural, as if this was simply an everyday thing I was doing, with no sense of despair, loss, or any other negative feeling that I might easily have experienced, now that I was about to be given a permanent false breast. I gave no thought to the fact that the prosthesis was a replacement for the natural breast I no longer had. Instead, I regarded it as a kind of early Christmas present, because I knew it would enhance my life. The softie was very difficult to keep in place, and once when we were out having a meal together it popped out of the neck of my top! Feigning nonchalance I'd shoved it quickly back down again, hoping nobody had noticed, and from then on I secured it with a safety pin. It was good to know that after today I wouldn't have to worry about that sort of thing happening any more.

As well as the bras I'd also been told to take a close fitting tee shirt, so the nurse could see my outline when I tried out different models of breast form. She asked me which bra I wanted to wear for the fitting. I had a sports model, a very beautiful lacy one and a plainer, everyday type of bra. I chose the everyday bra, which I had to put on with the strap on my affected side down, to enable the prosthesis to be inserted into the pocket. The nurse showed me how to do this, before pulling the strap up for me, checking the bra for fit, comparing the pocketed side with the other. We tried three different prostheses. They were all filled with silicone gel and I was surprised at how heavy they felt when I held them in my hands, as opposed to when I was wearing them. The nurse said everyone notices this when they first handle a permanent breast form, but that when it came to actually wearing one, everything felt well balanced. The first one we tried was too narrow, the third didn't look 'fleshy' enough in the middle part of my chest, but the second was just right. I couldn't believe how I looked when I stood in front of the full-length mirror. I appeared to have a better figure than I'd had before the mastectomy! I put on the tee shirt and the nurse took a good look at me, before asking me to look at my reflection from both sides to make sure the outline was what I wanted. She was delighted with my fitting, saying it was one of the most successful she'd ever performed. I wasn't used to seeing myself with such a perfect shape because my left breast had always been slightly smaller than the right, and at first I felt my 'new breast' was too big. But after a minute or two I could see it was the same size as my natural breast, and I was thrilled with it.

I put on the sweater I'd been wearing. The contour of my bust was perfect. I was overjoyed, hugging the nurse and thanking her for giving me this lovely shape. I felt proud and happy to be looking like this for the first time ever. I was like a little child who'd gone to see Santa Claus and been given a really nice present! The nurse was as pleased for me as I was for myself, and gave me a special box to keep my prosthesis in, together with a cotton cover for it, to protect it from damage by perspiration. The box had a moulded space inside, into which the prosthesis fitted so that its shape would be retained. The nurse told me to wash it after each wearing, and to treat it just like any other part of my body. I'd have to avoid sharp objects, animal claws and the like, but apart from this I could wear it with confidence, enjoying the natural feel and appearance of it. It felt so much like a real breast that it was impossible to tell the two apart. I couldn't wait to show Pete, and when I left the hospital I felt so excited I thought I would burst.

The next bus into town came along only seconds after I'd reached the bus stop. I sat on the back seat so that I could peer down the neck of my sweater without anyone seeing what I was doing. I was amazed by what I saw, and couldn't stop looking at myself. It was just too good to be true. I'd never expected to look like this after my mastectomy, and my self-esteem soared sky high.

When I met up with Pete I threw open my jacket, eager to show him how I looked. I didn't care who noticed, all that mattered to me was that Pete could see. Oblivious to everyone around us I took his hand and placed it over the left side of my bosom. He couldn't believe how real the prosthesis looked and felt. Noticing his eyes had begun to fill up I suggested we got on with our Christmas shopping. Hand in hand we strolled through town, and all through the day I kept looking down at myself as we walked along. I knew I had a choice now, of whether (for appearance's sake) to have a full bust again or to be just as I was. I approved of myself in either case. I didn't need a perfect bosom to be the real me, but it was nice to know I now had the option. My dignity was important to me, it had never been taken away from me just because I'd had a mastectomy, but today the new breast I'd received gave my self-respect a real boost. It had been an excellent day for me so far, but the best was yet to come.

I love what most people refer to as 'coincidences'. I prefer to call them synchronicities, because I believe nothing happens by chance and that everything is pre-destined. Before we went home I wanted to see my friend Sue, to show her what I looked like in my bra. We parked the car near the office where she works and I rushed in. "What do you think?" I asked, holding up my sweater after making sure her boss wasn't around. Sue left her desk, dumbstruck and with tears in her eyes. "Oh Chris, it's wonderful!" she exclaimed, surprised to see how realistic everything looked. I invited her to feel my false breast. She was amazed, saying she couldn't tell that it wasn't real. She was so pleased for me, giving me an enormous hug. Then, without warning or hesitation, Sue pulled up her own top, to show me she was wearing an identical bra to the one I had on! We both thought this was incredible, and how we laughed together. Sue and I enjoyed the loudest, longest laugh we'd had in ages. As I left her, she gave me a wonderful smile, and I thought it was great that my friend was so genuinely happy for me.

This wasn't the end of it. Walking towards our parked car was Joyce, another very close friend who had breast cancer, chemotherapy and radiotherapy a year before I did. We are related through marriage, because our husbands are cousins. Joyce and I had supported one another throughout our respective treatments. We were thrilled to meet and ran straight into each other's arms. Joyce knew I'd gone for the fitting and asked how I'd got on, grinning at me like the proverbial Cheshire Cat. I showed her. "You look fantastic!" she exclaimed, adding he words "I love mine!" as she disappeared into the nearby florists. She looked radiant. I felt radiant. We both had just cause and reason to be radiant, for we are warriors and had come through our battles scarred, but victorious. For us to have met by sheer chance like that seemed uncanny, just as if it had been meant to happen. But there was even more to come. Turning to look through the door of the adjacent chemist's shop I was astonished to see another friend who had staunchly supported me since my mastectomy. Her name happens to be Joyce too, and she is also related to Pete. This Joyce had often sent me flowers when I went for my chemotherapy. Her kind thoughts had touched us both very deeply, and we'd affectionately nicknamed her 'The Flower Lady'. I burst through the shop door, grabbed her, and with the words "Guess what I've got!" threw open my jacket again. The reaction had to be seen for it to be believed; her face was a picture, her mouth was wide open and she looked absolutely stunned. I loved it! "Go on, feel it." I said. With a schoolgirl's giggle, Joyce extended a forefinger and gave my breast a tentative prod. "Not like that, feel it properly," I said, grasping her hand and placing her open palm on my new breast. There, in the middle of the busy shop, she gave it an enormous squeeze! We both enjoyed the laughter too much to care about anyone looking at us. Then, we hugged, and wished each other a Happy Christmas. It was wonderful for me to have seen the three women with whom I share a meaningful friendship and who had all been so supportive. The meetings couldn't possibly have been coincidental. Something as wondrous as that could only have been destined to be. I was ecstatic as we drove home. We had yet to celebrate Pete's birthday, and I had something very special planned for him.

When we got home I went upstairs and took off the bra, placing the breast form safely in its box. After dinner I asked Pete to stay in the living room because I had a surprise for him. I went upstairs and took my prosthesis out of its box. I felt a little unsure of it as I handled it for the first time by myself, afraid of damaging it. The outer covering is thin and transparent, and I was concerned that I might snag it on my fingernails. But it slid into the pocket in my lace bra with no trouble at all. I put on a long white petticoat that was a good match for the bra, and looked very romantic. Then I took a large sheet of pink crepe paper that I'd bought days ago, especially for this occasion, along with a couple of metres of pink ribbon. I wrapped the pink paper around myself, tying it in place with the ribbon, making a large bow at the front of my chest. I put my hair up, making small bows from the left over pieces of ribbon, and pinned these into it. I looked like a pink Christmas fairy, and thoroughly enjoyed being so outrageous! The colour was significant, because pink ribbons are worn to commemorate Breast Cancer Awareness Month in October. The pink ribbon has become the enduring emblem of the organisation 'Breast Cancer Care' and I knew Pete would understand the relevance of the colour I'd decked myself out in. Incredulously I stared at my reflection in the mirror for a moment or two, before giving the prosthesis a little naming ceremony. I named it 'Bosom Buddy'!

I was shaking with excitement as I went downstairs, wondering how Pete would react when he saw me. I crept into the living room, trying to be as quiet as I could so he wouldn't hear the paper rustling. Asking him to keep his eyes closed I went to stand in front of the fire, in the light of the Christmas tree. My heart was in my mouth as I said "Open your eyes now, I've got a special birthday present for you to unwrap." Pete was speechless, not knowing whether to smile or cry. He stood up, came over to me and hugged me as if he didn't ever want to let me go. "Go on, open your present," I urged, impatient for him to see what was underneath the paper. Without saying a word Pete carefully undid the bow, slipping off the ribbon and slowly unwinding the paper from my body. I was so full of emotion that I burst into tears because I'd been preparing myself for this moment for days, and was desperate for a reaction from him. He said he was unable to cry because he'd done so much of that, and that even though I looked lovely in the bra, I was beautiful enough for him without it. His face was full of sympathy and concern. I hadn't realised Pete was seriously worried that I might be having a problem with myself, and thought I might be trying to disguise this beneath a show of bravado. I was desperate to convince him that this wasn't so, feeling upset that he was thinking along those lines. But because his concerns have always been for how I feel, how I react to things, the effect of situations on my emotions, I understood the way his mind was working. I was relieved to hear him say he believed me when I told him I was simply very happy to be able to wear such a beautiful bra so well, that I didn't think I only looked okay if I *was* wearing it, which was what he believed at first. Pete realised, then, what sort of a reaction I'd wanted, and made sure I got it!

That night I stayed up late to wrap a few Christmas presents, pondering on the day's events, feeling so content with everything in my life. It had been a perfect day in all ways. I loved the entire world as I re-lived the happenings in sequence; the fitting, the feeling of pride I had in myself, the meeting with those special friends, and Pete's reaction to the surprise I had planned. I couldn't have asked for a more satisfying or rewarding day, and gave many thanks as I sat in the firelight. The next day was the eve of the Midwinter Solstice. The time to put chaos and darkness behind us and, with the return of the Sun, to emerge from that darkness energised and purified by the coming of the light. Life would soon be stirring in the earth again as the days began to lengthen. Life was certainly stirring in me. I knew that the approaching solstice would hold great meaning and significance for us; that its promise of hope and new awakenings would encourage and inspire us. I went to bed that night with thankfulness in my heart, and joy and serenity in my spirit.

Thirty-Two

After Christmas I went for chemo 3A, on 28th December. My blood count was comparatively high and I was feeling well, with a good supply of energy. But then things changed dramatically. I was admitted to hospital on New Year's Eve with a severe and crippling pain in my upper abdomen on the left side, coupled with shortness of breath. Because of the nature and position of the pain, the doctors suspected I had a blood clot in my lung, and I had to have a chest X ray. Thankfully this showed my lungs were clear, but the pain remained a mystery. My tummy was pressed, poked, prodded and listened to with a stethoscope. The diagnosis was eventually made; I was suffering from nothing more than chronic constipation! This can also be a side effect of chemotherapy, and I was given some medication to take home, to help relieve the problem. But the pain and breathlessness persisted, and when I went for 3B on 4th January the oncology doctor said there could be a blood clot in my lung, despite the clear X ray. He insisted I had a ventilation scan (VQ scan) saying this was the only reliable method of showing up a clot. I was happy to go along with his advice, and the doctor telephoned the radiology department to book a slot for me to have one that morning.

A VQ scan is done in two parts. The first part scans the airways. Radioactive mist is inhaled before a picture of the lungs is taken. I had to place my lips and teeth round a mouthpiece that was attached to a long tube. The mouthpiece has to be gripped tightly with the teeth, so that the lips make a seal around it. Then the mist is inhaled through the mouth and into the lungs. I had to breathe the mist in for five minutes, while pictures of my lungs were taken. Then I sat with my chest against a metal plate, and further images were taken, of the front, back and each side of my chest.

After this section of the scan was complete I went for my chemotherapy, because there needed to be a time lapse between parts one and two. Sitting in the chemo waiting area I noticed a young woman leaving the treatment room, and recognised her as a pupil I had taught at school years ago. She was gone in a flash, before I had time to speak to her. I felt concerned, wondering what type of cancer she was suffering from and how serious her condition might be. To see someone so young having treatment for cancer really does make one aware that life should never be wasted. I had witnessed so much courage and determination in the other patients. Memories of these heroic individuals will remain with me always, most especially the youngsters.

The chemo went well and afterwards we headed for the cafeteria, to pass the time before the second part of my scan was due. We'd just sat down when we noticed an old friend of mine whom I hadn't seen for at least ten years, sitting at another table, and I went over to speak to him. He had brought his sister to hospital for a check up, and came to sit at our table while he waited for her. We enjoyed catching up on each other's news, and this made my day complete. My chemo had been straightforward, with no difficulties regarding blood count. I was having a scan to ensure I had no blood clot, and had met a friend whom I hadn't seen in ages. It had been such a productive day that I thought the scan result was bound to be okay too, and didn't worry or even think about having a blood clot in my lung, because I felt pretty certain everything was fine. I was just grateful that I was being so well looked-after.

The chemo nurse had left the cannula in my vein, ready for the second part of the scan. This saved me the discomfort of having to go through the insertion process again. She had bandaged it firmly, covering my entire hand, to guard against the needle coming out. Once back in the scanning department I had to lie on a bed as the radiographer removed the bandaging and injected the radioactive solution, along with some saline that was, she said, "to flush it through." Images were scanned, and then we were asked to wait for the results.

The scan showed I had no blood clot; the discomfort was still being caused by nothing more serious than the tummy problem. Pete and I rejoiced, for not only was this very good news, but also we'd reached that enormous landmark on which our sights had been set for so long. We were halfway through my treatment now, and it felt terrific! From now on, it really was countdown time.

Thirty-Three

From this point onwards I began to feel very ill, the side effects worsened and I didn't know how I was going to get through the rest of the treatment. I spent most of the time huddled in my 'Chemo Corner'. Pete had fixed an extending reading lamp to the wall near my armchair, and bought an electric fan to put on the table beside it. The table has a shelf, on which I kept my supply of chocolate-covered ginger. So I was able to read in comfort, indulge my chocolate craving and relieve my hot sweats by switching on the fan! The fan was gorgeous; its cooling effect was pure ecstasy. 'Chemo Corner' became my very own special little sanctuary.

I felt so tired, absolutely exhausted, just wanting to go to sleep. My arms and legs felt so heavy that I couldn't even stand sometimes. I felt sick, faint, with no energy at all. Sometimes Pete had to help me get out of my chair because I was so weak. I shuffled along with one foot behind the other. It was as though I couldn't do anything at all except 'just be.' I was ravenous, and craved food. It felt like nothing I've ever experienced before, much worse than a bad dose of 'flu', and that always knocks the stuffing out of me. Sometimes I couldn't speak any louder than in a whisper, because talking was just too much of an effort. All I wanted to do was flop in the chair. When I needed to move around the house at these times I held onto Pete because I was so unsteady. But things weren't as dire as this all the time, just for a few days after the chemo. The worst days were the first three or four. After that, the state of affairs always gradually improved, and by the time my next dose was due I usually felt fairly well again.

Throughout my treatment we never lost our sense of humour. It helped to make the situation more bearable, and we always tried to see the funny side of things. For example, just after we'd reached the halfway point in my treatment Pete hurt his back, and had to use a walking stick because of the pain he was in. I was feeling particularly bad at this time, relying on Pete to help me stagger around the house. On one occasion we were on our way to the bathroom when we caught site of ourselves in the hall mirror. There we stood, Pete bent double with his stick in one hand, me dangling limply under his other arm, looking as if I'd been made up to play a role in a horror movie! We looked at each other and just creased up with laughter at ourselves. It was laughter and absolute daftness at times that got us through this difficult period. Without humour, neither of us would have been able to withstand it as well as we did. Together we laughed and smiled our way through it, whenever we could. And of course, there were those times when, together, we cried.

No matter how bad I felt during the course of my treatment, I knew I had much to be thankful for. Some of my fellow patients looked so poorly, and very frail. Several had lost their hair. I saw both men and women who were completely bald, and some women wearing wigs, scarves or hats to cover their hair loss. I considered myself very fortunate not to have lost my hair, but because my dose of chemo was only half-strength it didn't fall out. Back home some people would remark, "You haven't lost your hair then," little knowing that this was because I was unable to tolerate a full dose of chemo, and also that the type of chemo I was on doesn't always induce complete hair loss. At the start of my treatment I plucked up courage and went to a good stylist who cut my hair quite a bit shorter than the shoulder length it had always been. The cut wasn't before time, because my hair was in very bad condition. The hairdresser said that if I had it trimmed and layered, any thinning that resulted from the treatment wouldn't be as noticeable. He was absolutely right, and I was pleased with the cut because my hair became full of volume and natural wave, appearing thick and healthy all through my treatment, although it did thin a little. Hair soon grows, and to have it shortened was the least of my worries.

Once, during an unusually long wait for my chemo, we spent the time listening to a lovely lady as she told us her story. Chemotherapy was helping to prolong her life. Her tale was heart wrenching, especially because she was so brave, so cheerful, always with a smile for us and a "How are you feeling today, dear?" each time we met in the waiting area. She never complained about her own situation, her first concern always being for others. This woman was remarkable, a true inspiration, and we will never forget her, or her husband, shouldering so great a burden and supporting his wife through her illness as best he could under the circumstances. The people we met were enduring so much, willingly putting up with all the anxiety and discomfort in hopes that their lives would be saved or lengthened. I can truthfully say that the experiences I had in that oncology unit led me to regard the time I spent there as being one of the most valuable, most enlightening periods of my entire life, because it enabled me to understand the physical and emotional anguish that cancer patients have to bear. For us to be able to show someone who is suffering that we truly empathise with him or her is almost certainly one of the greatest things we can ever do for that person. Each human conflict, crisis and drama we have to endure has its value, in terms of the empathy we gain from the experience, even though at times we may question why, or feel bitterly angry. Empathy is the means through which we can help others realise they are not alone in their suffering. It is the only qualification we need to be able to truthfully say, "I know how you are feeling. I understand what you are going through, because I have borne your pain."

Thirty-Four

On 28th January, three days after dose 4A, I reached my lowest point. The chemo nurses had warned me to expect this because evidently it is usual for this to happen, but I'd tried to convince myself it wouldn't happen to me. At the start of my treatment I had been confronted with the newness of it. Coping with it was a challenge, almost an adventure, which I dealt with fairly easily because my determination to stand up to the treatment overrode the actuality. Now it was tough going, thinking about the disease I'd had and wondering why I should have to put up with all this. Emotional reactions were easily triggered, and I became reluctant to continue with the chemotherapy as time went on.

When the nurses told me it was normal for me to feel like this I was reassured, because I'd begun to wonder if it was due to me losing my courage. A combination of factors led to my weakening state of mind. For me, as for most people, chemotherapy was neither easy nor pleasant. The way it depleted my energy, making me feel good for nothing for days or weeks after, didn't do much to make me feel too thrilled about going for 4B on 1st February, although after I'd had it I felt great, knowing there were only four more doses left for me to have. The vein in my wrist was becoming tender and I felt queasy each time I thought of the needle going in, wondering if I'd be able to stand up to the rest of my treatment or whether I would completely crack under the strain of it before I reached the end.

Pete was upset at seeing me so down. He did all he could to try to cheer me up, saying he could never know exactly how I felt, being unable to empathise, but that he would do anything he could to make things easier for me. I told him that all I needed was for him to love me. Love and caring were the only things that helped, not only from Pete but also from friends and everyone we knew. Each time someone greeted me, or us, with the words "How are you, how's the treatment going?" we knew they were not only thinking about us but also really caring. Their interest meant a lot. We were so amazed by the number of phone calls that I kept a log of them. One look at that long list of names never failed to encourage me and renew my determination to stick things out. I could see that we had many allies in this battle we were engaged in. In my imagination these wonderful people became the Amazon's loyal band of followers, a group of men and women trooping close behind, ready to pick her up when she stumbled or was wounded, gathering the weapons she dropped as she fell, placing them firmly in her hands ready for the next onslaught. Visualisation is a powerful tool, as is meditation, and I utilised both to the full during those months, using the support from all the good people in our lives to create strong, mental images of myself on my way to victory over that formidable opponent, the cancer I was striving to defeat.

Morning and night I looked up at the sky to watch the pink-footed geese as they flew overhead, in the mornings to their feeding grounds on nearby fields away from the coast, and back again in the evenings to the shore. The sight and sound of those birds really inspired me because their determination was so strong. Instinctively they flew hundreds of miles, year after year. I would watch the scores of V-formations in sheer wonder, telling myself that if these creatures could accomplish so much, enduring such harsh extremes of weather as they travelled the vast distances, I too could put up a good fight and bear the remainder of my treatment. I looked forward to seeing the geese every day, because of the courage they inspired in me. It later struck me that my chemotherapy was due to finish just as they would be departing for northern lands in the early spring, ready to breed again, and I interpreted this as an omen, that I would get through it all with their help, and that when this was accomplished I would bid them farewell with gratitude for their strengthening presence throughout that long, dark time, when their welcome appearance in the winter skies, always heralded by their unmistakable honking calls, was my sign that the future held promise of much brighter days to come.

Thirty-Five

Valentine's Day arrived, and we'd planned to go out for a meal that evening. I was really looking forward to getting away from the house for a while, but typically a phone call from the hospital put paid to that idea. My blood had been sent off the day before, and the test indicated a seriously low neutrophil count. I was advised to stay at home and not to mix with people until the count rose, to take my temperature twice daily for a week, and to contact my GP's surgery to ask for a nurse to come to take some blood for a further test in three days time. Evidently it wasn't a good idea for me to go to the surgery because of the risk of infection from the other patients. It was my birthday later that week, and we cancelled our plans for both occasions. I was really disappointed at not being able to go out on my birthday, or even to have visitors, because of the risk of infection. There was a lot of illness about, and many people had bugs and colds. Friends left cards and gifts for me in our front porch and spoke to me through the window. I felt as if I'd got the Plague! But everyone saw the funny side of the situation, and later on our friend Robert really did give us something to smile about.

Answering the telephone in the early evening I heard Rob's cheerful voice. "Happy Birthday Chrissie, I'm outside your house." He'd used his mobile phone to tell us he was there! Rob refused to come anywhere near me because he had a terrible cold, so I went to the front window and saw him standing at our garden gate. He had left an enormous bouquet of flowers in our porch, and I was disappointed at being unable to thank him for them 'in person', so to speak. Pete and I chatted to him on the phone for a few minutes, before waving goodbye from the window. This birthday had a real 'cloak and dagger' atmosphere about it that was really quite amusing. But the isolation and avoidance of everyone was something I had to put up with because I had no choice. I'd been warned that if I caught an infection while my blood count was so low there would be a risk of it turning into septicaemia, and that if this were to happen it could have serious consequences for me. Although I tried not to think about that scenario I knew the threat was a very real one, which was why I followed all the advice I was given to the letter. As a substitute for going out for a meal, Pete got us fish and chips and we opened a bottle of wine, which was just as much of a treat, if not better, because we were in our own home where things were comfortable and cosy. As we sat in the firelight Pete told me he was proud of me, and proud to have me as his woman. "We're going to have some nice days," he said, "we'll do some lovely things, you'll see." I knew I had everything to live for. His name means 'The Rock' but my Pete is Mount Everest.

I was due to have 5A on 22nd February but it had to be delayed for the usual reason. During the waiting period I stayed at home for most of the time, still trying to avoid infections. On one particularly bright, sunny winter's day, when I was feeling a little more energetic than usual, I had an overwhelming urge to climb the cherry tree in our garden. For some reason I wanted to look at my environment from a bird's perspective, and I was surprised to find that I was able to haul myself up into the tree fairly easily. I found a comfortable place to sit and rested my back against a strong bough. It was sheltered and quite cosy sitting there, safely enclosed within the branches. From my perch I surveyed my world. It was wonderful to look down on it and see things from a different angle. The motivation to climb had been very strong, and I was glad I'd been unable to resist the compulsion. Even as a child I had never climbed a tree, and it was a tremendous accomplishment for me to have done so for the very first time now, at almost fifty years old!

Sitting there in the tree I felt young again, full of enthusiasm about life and the future, excited about living and being part of the wonderful world we inhabit. After about half an hour I clambered down. My energy had been recharged, and I felt as if I'd actually absorbed some of that tree's precious life force. I'd planted it as a young sapling fifteen years ago, and now it had repaid me for providing it with everything it needed to have enabled it to thrive and grow into the substantial adult it had become.

During the next fortnight the nurse came several times to take the blood samples because although chemo 5A had been reorganised for 1st March, my blood count wasn't high enough for me to have it until the 8th. I was feeling very low after spending so much time at home. The prospect of having to put up with more feeling ill and exhausted after the next lot of chemotherapy was daunting, and I really felt I'd had enough. I recalled the times when I would wake at night feeling so weak that I could hardly turn my head on the pillow, let alone get out of bed by myself. On one occasion I hadn't enough strength to even open my eyes for a minute or so, which was quite terrifying for both of us. When I was in this feeble state I staggered around the house like a zombie, and sometimes even breathing was difficult, almost too much of an effort. I was a horrible colour and I loathed it all.

When I spoke to the oncology doctor prior to my 5A treatment session I told him I couldn't face any more chemo and didn't wish to continue. His reaction to this was to give me a stern lecture, telling me that because of the nature of the cancer I'd had I should complete the course. He said research shows that four cycles of chemotherapy are good, providing some protection against recurrence, but that for women under the age of fifty, six cycles are better. He strongly advised me to have the chemo, but gave me the option to refuse treatment if I really felt I couldn't take any more. Evidently, some people do throw in the towel because they find the treatment so hard to bear. But I knew I ought to finish mine, despite how very ill it was making me feel. I'd come this far and it made no sense to stop now, when I was almost at the end of it. I agreed to go ahead with 5A, albeit half-heartedly, and the doctor was clearly relieved. He quickly checked me over, handed me an information sheet about my forthcoming radiotherapy, and sent me straight off for my treatment. I had the impression that he didn't intend giving me any extra time in which to change my mind!

As Pete and I climbed the stairs to the oncology treatment area I didn't feel very confident at all, wondering if I was physically up to having the chemo, and it turned out that I wasn't. When the nurse tried to cannulate, my vein wouldn't accept the needle because it had collapsed. This happens sometimes, when the veins become tender through all the punishment they take, but it was the first time it had ever happened to me, and the pain was so severe that I just broke down. The nurse was in tears as well, saying she felt terrible because she had hurt me. I told her not to worry, that I'd had a bad day and that I'd anticipated this difficulty with the chemo. I'd never given way to any discomfort before, but because I was so tense this time I couldn't help it. I asked the nurse to try again, because I was determined to have the chemo, no matter how painful the cannulation was going to be. She selected a different vein but the same thing happened. Both the oncology sisters told me it would be best for me not to have the chemo today, and to come back for 5A next week instead. But I wasn't prepared to give up so easily and insisted they tried just once more, asking if Pete could be allowed to sit beside me whilst they did so. One of them went to fetch him from the waiting area. After my first dose of treatment he hadn't been permitted to come into the chemo room with me any more because the space was small and there was a real danger of accidents. It was thought that people could easily trip over the drip stands, lengths of tubing and other essential items lying on the floor near the patients' chairs, and new guidelines had been drawn up with this in mind. But I was so upset by the pain and the general poor state I was in that I wanted Pete to be with me, knowing he would help me to be strong enough to withstand another attempt. As luck would have it, I was the only patient in the room at the time, and there was plenty of space for him to sit beside me. I buried my face in his sweater as both the nurses closely examined my hand, selecting a fresh vein to try.

This vein wouldn't accept the needle either. The pain was excruciating and the plan to give 5A was aborted. I became very upset about this. I felt I'd let everyone down, especially myself. The nurses were fantastic, telling me not to feel like that because they see this happen to people almost every day. The side effects of the chemo can make some people feel depressed and despondent the further on they get in the treatment. It would be reasonable for anyone to assume patients get more used to it as time goes on, but this isn't always the case. For me, the weakness, fatigue, the inability to move at times and all the fear associated with these effects of the treatment on my body and mind had taken their toll. I told myself not to feel ashamed, that even the bravest warrior cannot continue fighting without resting between battles. I realised that if I took things easy and looked after myself over the next seven days, retaining as much mental and physical stamina as I could, my vein would be able to withstand 5A next time. The dose was rescheduled for 15th March. I was given a sedative tablet to take one hour before my appointment, to make certain I would be as relaxed as possible so that the needle could be inserted easily and without too much discomfort. As a rule I felt no pain as such during the cannulation, just a feeling of something sliding into my wrist. The nurses were so gentle, skilled and experienced that it never really hurt at all. But I knew I'd have to try hard to forget the pain I'd had this time so as not to induce any mental block that might preclude my completing the rest of my treatment. It was far from easy because every time I thought about the experience I 'felt' the pain. During the following week I worked hard on myself, meditating and relaxing, trying desperately to erase the memory of it. On our way home Pete did his best to try to make me feel better, telling me I'd been brave to have made the effort to have the chemo, and that he was very proud of me: "Just because you tried and couldn't have it this doesn't mean you've failed. You were successful because you were so willing to try. You have nothing to be ashamed of because you couldn't have it this time. It was just that you were unable to because your body was tense and unwilling to take the needle today. Don't feel down, you made such a brave effort, so feel proud of yourself because of that." I thanked Pete for these words of encouragement, so full of insight and understanding, knowing how sincerely they had been spoken.

It was dark when we got home, and when Pete went into the kitchen to make us some tea I put my head on my arms on the mantelpiece and sobbed uncontrollably in front of the fire. I completely lost it then, for the first time ever. I couldn't stop crying, because I was feeling so dejected. Pete led me gently to the sofa, wrapping his strong arms around me as he asked me to listen to something very special that he wanted to say. His words were beautiful, and I will never forget them: "Think of us being a couple of birds, flying together over beaches, parks, mountains and lakes. Then as a couple of hares, running together in fields. Then a couple of whales in the sea, our huge tails flashing up from the water." Soothed and comforted I relaxed in his arms, my whole being infused with a deep feeling of inner peace. Later we watched a TV programme in bed together before I left him, going to sleep in the spare room. And in the morning I woke up to see SNOW!

Thirty-Six

I got up at once, washing and dressing as quickly as I could so that I could take our dog out before the snow stopped falling. Sky is a lovely animal, a crossbreed of Irish Wolfhound, Lurcher and German Shepherd, with beautiful long fur in every imaginable shade of grey. She leaped and bounded along, sniffing and snorting at the layer of snow on the ground, full of vitality and vigour, enjoying the experience to the full. I thought how marvellous life is, with so many natural wonders for us to find pleasure in, wishing, hoping and praying that I would live to enjoy many more wonderful winter days like this one. I gazed at the snow-laden branches of the trees, the white-blanketed fields in the distance, the darkening sky from which the snowflakes tumbled and whirled. I felt them settle on my face, and savoured the icy freshness as they landed on my tongue. I wanted to wring all I could out of this moment, to test each one of my senses to its limit. I'd seen, touched, tasted, and when I stopped to listen to the sounds of the woodland I noticed how quiet it was, how muffled and subdued. All was hushed as the snow fell. I breathed the cold air in deeply, filling my lungs. The magical scent of winter was unmistakable. I was filled with gratitude for this fabulous experience that I was enjoying so much, and for the life force within me that enabled me to appreciate and be receptive to all this natural beauty.

When we were back home I dried Sky off. The fur on her feet was matted with beads of frozen snow, which were impossible to remove. She lay on her bed and began to nibble at her toes, licking the ice wedged between them until it melted. This dog knows a great deal. Whenever I was low after my chemo she would sit with her head on my knee and a paw on my arm. Whenever I felt the need for the obligatory 'little cry', Sky was immediately beside me. Once, when I was really down and very tearful, she gently eased her shaggy head up under my left arm, resting her warm, furry body on my lap, her front paws around my hips. There she stayed for almost an hour. In her way she was holding me, telling me she loved me and trying to comfort me. It was as if Sky knew this side of my body needed healing. Whilst I was having chemo she was subdued, much quieter and far less boisterous than usual. When it was over she became her bouncy, lively self again, although still very gentle whenever she was near me. This remarkable animal played her part too, in my recovery.

One disappointment followed another as far as chemo 5A was concerned. After that failed attempt, it had to be delayed for a further three weeks because of my obstinate neutrophils. Even though six weeks had passed since I had 4B, this time they hadn't recovered very well at all, and it was really disheartening to have the chemo put off again and again. I was two-thirds of the way through it after 4B, with only another two complete cycles, or four doses, to go. My oncologist was only happy about me having the chemotherapy if my neutrophil count was 1.5 or higher, and it hovered around 0.8 for a considerable time between the fourth and fifth cycles, making chemo out of the question. All I could do was wait for my blood count to go up again.

At the beginning of my treatment I'd been very worried about catching infections, especially concerned about visitors bringing them into the house. Pete was so worried about bringing infections home from work that he ate his lunch alone, avoiding the staff canteen. With hindsight this seemed almost ridiculous, as if we were taking things to extremes, but at the time, when we'd been warned of the seriousness of the risks I faced, it made sense to be careful. There is an enormous difference between being paranoid about keeping safe, and being far-sighted and sensible. I wasn't obsessed with avoiding infections, but was as cautious as it was possible for anyone to be. I stuck a notice on our front door, politely asking anyone who either had an infection or had been in contact with one to phone us instead of knocking and expecting to come in, and I'd asked Lucy for suggestions as to how best to word it. The idea she proposed was curt and to the point, although not exactly what I had in mind. ("If you've got a cold, p--- off!") I doubled up with laughter at this, envisaging the affronted reactions such plain speaking would have provoked. Of course Lucy hadn't been serious, although I must admit to half-thinking her explicit suggestion was rather apt, given the state of mind I was in at that time.

As I became more used to the effects of the chemotherapy I was less frightened of catching anything, and didn't allow the risk to take over my life. Whereas at first I felt extremely vulnerable, by the time I'd completed the fourth cycle I felt much less anxious and just like any other person, really, who runs the usual risk of catching those winter colds and infections to which most people succumb at that time of the year. I only caught one infection during my entire treatment period, and that was after the completion of cycle two when I picked up a respiratory bug. My doctor gave me a course of strong antibiotics that knocked it on the head very quickly. Just knowing effective medication was available in the event that I became ill was a comfort, and helped me to be less preoccupied with striving to avoid situations and people that might pose a threat.

On 15th March I was able to have 5A, and I felt so pleased after I'd had it, even though I knew I'd be feeling ill for several days after. I focused my thoughts on the fact that this was the start of the last third of my chemo. Twelve days later I had 5B, although if my blood had taken any longer than this to recover I would have had to start again with 5A. Thankfully my count picked up enough for me to have the B dose on 27th March, leaving only one more cycle to complete. By this time the side effects had really pulled me down. Besides the nausea and weakness every bone, joint, muscle and limb in my body ached. I'd been told not to take painkillers because they would mask any rise in my body temperature, and this still needed to be closely watched. My feet were especially painful and I could hardly bear to put any weight on them because the bones hurt so much. I longed for the end of my treatment to come, and by this time I was well and truly living in the slow lane, taking my time over everything I did, aiming to conserve as much physical and mental energy as I could so that I would be as fit as possible and able to have my sixth and final cycle of chemotherapy when it was due in three weeks time. The journey was almost over, and the light at the end of that long, dark road was slowly but surely coming into view.

Thirty-Seven

Pete and I were by this time 'old hands' in the realm of philosophical discussion. We would spend hours talking about all kinds of things, and on one occasion I asked him if he could explain to me exactly how he felt when we were told I had breast cancer:

"I was never afraid, really, of what it (the cancer) was, because the consultant instilled confidence in me. I felt confident because of the way he'd put it across to us, and in what he'd told us. That's why I wanted to hear everything he had to say, so that I clearly understood it all. I understood that it had been found early, and fundamentally I put all my faith in him because of the way he acted over it. My main upset was for you, how I thought it was going to make you feel. It was like another hurdle at the end of a long line of them, having already had so much trouble with your health. My real concern was how you were going to cope with it. I'd seen you get so upset about things in the past, and this worried me more than anything. I could see it really grinding you down, judging from previous experience."

It is often true to say that many of us tend to allow the minor difficulties in life to get us down to a far greater extent than we do the more serious crises that come along to test us. When we are confronted with a real catastrophe, all our less significant cares and woes tend to disappear overnight. I understood what Pete was saying. The value of having a positive mental attitude to life and life's problems can never be over-estimated. Some things are just not worth the energy we use in worrying about them. Why give our power away to something that really doesn't matter, when we need to hang onto as much of it as we can so that when a real crisis happens, we have enough to see us through?

Because cancer threatens life, sufferers need every ounce of positive thought they can summon. I believe this need becomes a powerful drive that compels people with cancer and other serious diseases to develop an irresistible determination to survive. I was fortunate in that I stood a fairly good chance of being cured of my breast cancer. But I was never complacent, and never have been to this day. I know I have been touched by a potentially fatal disease, and I have been told that for several years yet I must be vigilant, alert to changes anywhere in my body, not only in my remaining breast. Despite this I continue to trust in my belief that all will be well, providing I take good care of myself. Each new day is a bonus, and I strive to give and to gain as much happiness as I can during every single one. Before my breast cancer I always regarded each new dawn as a blessing. The fact that I had this disease did nothing whatsoever to alter my spiritual beliefs in any way. It only served to strengthen them, to convince me even more that the things I believe in, the natural wonders of life that I revere, and the sense of values that prioritises these things, are right, for me.

Pete and I could hardly believe it when the day came for me to begin the sixth and final cycle of my chemotherapy. The 'A' dose had again been delayed for one week, but I didn't feel as upset about this as I'd done on previous occasions because I knew I was almost at the end of it. On 24th April I had 6A, and 6B was booked for 1st May. Ironically, this was an appropriate and significant day on which to have my very last dose of chemo. The festival of Beltane is celebrated at this time, and my thoughts were drawn to the concept of Purification by Fire. I had certainly walked between the flames to get to where I now was. At Beltane we see the Earth really coming alive; the living, pulsing energy is at its strongest, in man, beast and plant. It is a time of fertility, good luck and creativity, a time to be joyful, to dance and be merry, and to celebrate one's personal freedom. But I was to celebrate even more than this. In addition, my celebration was also of my return to normal life, my rising from the ashes of the past seven long months. The completion of my chemotherapy meant all these things to me. Thinking about the cancer I'd had, knowing what it is like to have chemotherapy, I almost felt as if I'd been shown what lies 'on the other side'. In all ways the experience had truly been the long, dark night of my soul. But the clear, bright morning was about to dawn.

On that final treatment day I had my blood taken at the hospital at ten o'clock. Then, Pete and I went into town for a couple of hours, to kill time until the results of the test were available. I was on edge all the while, feeling very agitated, longing to get the chemo over with. I couldn't relax because I was preoccupied with thinking about my blood test result. This was such an important day in my life, and our lives, seeing the culmination of over half a year of struggling to endure something that, although its purpose was to save my life, caused me to feel so ill that at times I felt I couldn't bear it. Now, here I stood on the threshold of victory, and all I wanted to do was to run through the door of the chemo room and seize that victory with both hands. The waiting was terrible.

The chemo nurse had asked me to phone her at midday, so that she could let me know if my blood count was high enough for me to have my treatment. The town centre was very busy, and frantically I searched for a quiet place from which to call her on our mobile phone. Eventually I found a disused shop. I huddled in the doorway, my back to the crowds, oblivious to everyone and everything around me except my link to the nurse through the phone in my trembling hands. I rang the hospital and asked the receptionist to connect me. Pete hovered nearby, aware of how uptight I was. I was so preoccupied with knowing my blood results that I'd hardly been able to speak a word to him. My mind was full of one thing only, whether I would be able to have my final dose of chemo today or not. I was obsessed with this thought, to the exclusion of everything else because the answer to this question was the most important thing in my life at that time. As soon as I heard the nurse's cheerful tone of voice I knew my blood was okay: "Your neutrophils are 1.88 today Chrissie. Come on in and let's get it over with!" Tears streamed down my face as I thanked her for the good news. The relief was so great that I couldn't stop crying. People stared at me but I didn't care. They had no idea of the strain I'd been under, nor of the elation I felt on being told I could now have my twelfth and final dose of chemo. Pete hugged me warmly, and as we walked hand in hand to the car park I almost dragged him along in my impatience to get back to the hospital. I was so intent on getting there that all I wanted to do was run as fast as I could to the car! The exhilaration took my breath away, and it was all I could do to stay on my feet as we reached the car park because by that time I was almost collapsing with excitement.

When we arrived in the waiting area outside the chemo room my heart was pounding so hard I thought it would stop. The nurse called me in soon after we'd sat down. Pete was beaming. "See you soon" he said. I replied that I wouldn't be long, and entered the chemo room for the last time.

I sat down in the chair with a huge lump in my throat. I had made it! After today I would have to endure this treatment no longer. It was difficult for me to believe that this really was the end. Was I at last going to be able to look forward to feeling well again? Was there really to be no more horrible nausea, weakness, absolute exhaustion and sheer inability to even enjoy drawing breath? Nothing in my entire life could ever compare with this, nothing I'd ever experienced before was as hard, as draining and as daunting as the chemotherapy had been, for me. Yet here I was, seven months down that long and arduous road, at the finishing post. It all felt like a dream, unreal and almost imaginary. As the nurse wiped my wrist over the place where she was to insert the cannula I returned abruptly to reality. Despite my earlier excitement I was now calm and relaxed, because I knew I had to be.

The needle went in painlessly, and the treatment was given. As the contents of the third syringe flowed into my vein, it all became too much for me and I gave in to the emotion. The nurse hugged me, understanding how I was feeling. I thanked both the chemo nurses for everything they had done for me and for Pete, although words weren't adequate enough to express the volume of our gratitude. We felt we owed these people so much. I'd bought an enormous jar of chocolates for all the oncology staff, and handed this to my nurse along with a card addressed to everyone. She and her colleague each gave us both a parting kiss and a hug, and the two of them stood at the door of the chemo room waving goodbye to us as we walked away. Reaching the entrance to the stairway that led down to the ground floor I gave one final look back. The nurses had disappeared into the room, to continue their work with another patient. Someone who was about to have their first dose of chemo, who was feeling just like I did all those months ago; apprehensive, uncertain of what to expect, anxious and insecure. Like me, she would come to the end of it one day, and my wish for her was that when she reached that point she would feel as full of hope and optimism as I did now.

The entrance to the stairs was like a magical portal leading to the rest of my life. I had learned so much during my chemotherapy treatment, about myself, about Pete, and about everyone in our lives. But most of all I learned that I was a far stronger woman than I'd ever allowed myself to believe. I knew that my future would no longer be tainted by the inhibiting anxiety and tension that had dominated my life in the past. I felt FREE! I thought that if it had taken my having breast cancer to banish these constraining, repressing influences that had plagued me for as long as I could remember, and given me the unwavering strength and self assurance that I now possessed, then I could almost bless it. My life, and our lives from now on, would be lived according to how I, and we wanted to live them. Now, and for the rest of our life together, it was *our* time.

Thirty-Eight

My radiotherapy began on 29th May, almost exactly nine months after the mastectomy. The oncologist told me it would be easy compared to the chemotherapy, and she was right. The most difficult part was the travelling, because like many others we had to drive to a much larger hospital in Cambridge every weekday for three weeks, because the one I'd been attending for my chemotherapy has no facility to give radiotherapy. The journey took a couple of hours each way, and the daily distance we had to travel was just over a hundred and fifty miles.

Radiotherapy is a process by which powerful X rays are used to destroy cancer cells. In my case, having had a complete mastectomy, the radiotherapy was applied to my chest along and all around the scar line. This was done to ensure, as far as possible, that the growth potential of any remaining cancer cells would be eradicated.

First came the planning session on the day before my treatment started. This was carried out on a simulator, a replica of the machine used to project the rays. The planning is crucial because each time the radiotherapy is given, the patient has to be in exactly the same position, so that the rays target the treatment area with consistent accuracy. I had to take my top and bra off, then lie on my back under the simulator with a cushion under my knees, my arms bent up and my wrists supported, just as I would do when having the actual treatment. During the planning session precise measurements were recorded, both of the area to be treated and of the position of my body on the bed. This process was guided by laser beams, which projected red light onto the treatment area on my chest. The radiographers made a series of marks on my skin with a pen, and when they had finished, my chest looked like a page from a road atlas! When everything was correctly lined-up the information was displayed on monitors in the room. It would be screened whenever I went for my treatment, enabling the radiographers to ensure that I was correctly placed each time. The planning procedure took about half an hour, and during this time I had to keep absolutely still so that the measurements would remain constant.

My oncologist came into the room then, to check that all was satisfactory. She verified that everything was "spot on" and said I could now have my tattoos!

Because it is so vital that radiotherapy is applied to the same area of the body during each treatment session, permanent marking is essential. I was aware of this before I went for the planning session, knowing also that the tattoos would be so minute they would hardly show. (But when the oncologist mentioned the word I couldn't resist asking for a design brochure so that I could choose the one I wanted!) What I ended up with was scarcely visible; two tiny dark blue dots the size of small pinheads were tattooed on my chest at either end of a line drawn across it, one in the centre and the other on my left side beneath my arm. The process was absolutely painless and only slightly uncomfortable. Each tattoo took no more than a few seconds of time. Afterwards, the radiographers gave me some general advice on how to care for my skin during and after the treatment, warning me to cover up my chest and always use sun block because there would be an increased risk of sunburn to the treatment area not only now, but also for the rest of my life. I wasn't to use any deodorants at all during the treatment period and for a fortnight afterwards, after which I could use one providing it was alcohol free. Only baby talc and baby soap were permitted, with a definite "no" to perfumed foam baths, bath salts and other scented products.

Then began the long haul to Cambridge and back. Pete and I made an event of it, to help relieve the tedium of the journey. When we passed certain landmarks on the way, we each had a sweet. Nearer to Cambridge we parked in a secluded lay-by near open fields to have a cup of tea from our flask. On the way home we stopped to enjoy the picnic we took with us each day. But although we tried to make the long journey as interesting as we could, it was exhausting, and by the time the three weeks were up we'd had enough. I found it extremely uncomfortable travelling so far at that time of year because it was very hot, and this exacerbated the sweats and hot flashes. I covered my chest with a white cotton top during the journeys, because the sun shone directly on me as I sat in the car next to Pete, and I was very careful not to get burnt. I drank litres of water every day to avoid dehydrating in the heat, which was fairly intense.

The radiotherapy was easy. All I had to do was lie very still and let it happen. It took a little while for the radiographers to get me into the correct place on the bed each time. Even the slightest movement I made was enough to disturb my body position to the extent that it had to be re-aligned, and I had to remain absolutely motionless the whole time. It wasn't a good idea to sneeze or cough! The radiographers told me not to try to assist them by moving myself, but to just relax and allow them to shuffle and shove me into place. When they'd got me into the correct position they left the room, leaving me alone whilst the treatment was given. They could see me through the screen behind which they sat, and I was also able to communicate with them if at any time I needed to (which I didn't). The setting-up was always done with the lights off, so that the radiographers could see the laser beams. As they left the room the lights were switched on, and I was able to gaze at a beautiful mural painted on the ceiling over the bed. The picture was of an oak tree, with songbirds in the branches. The colours were lovely and the image was very restful. I love trees, particularly oaks, and thought how apt it was that I could look at a picture of one whilst I had my treatment.

The radiotherapy machine rotated around and above my body, to enable the rays to be directed from both sides, first from the left, then from the right. Each blast of radiation lasted for one minute, and between the changes of the angle of the machine the staff checked my position to make sure I hadn't moved. I experienced nothing but the humming sound the machine emitted as the rays were being directed to my chest. There was no pain, no sense of tingling or burning, no discomfort at all, in fact. As far as after effects were concerned, there was none of the nausea and debilitating weakness I suffered whilst on the chemo, and I didn't burn as such, even though I have red hair and fair skin. After a few days my skin started to itch, and by the end of the treatment a pale pink rectangular patch was clearly visible where the radiation had been applied. Aqueous Cream was recommended for moisturising the skin over the treatment area. This helped to ease the itching, but several weeks after my treatment had finished I found Aloe Vera gel to be very effective, for this has a cooling effect and is often used to relieve sunburn. Although it may not suit everyone, I found it worked very well for me.

For a few months after the radiotherapy had finished I experienced shooting, searing pains across the left half of my chest, which was a little disturbing, but the pain was sporadic as opposed to continuous. I had been warned to expect this, and when it occurred I tried to relax into it rather than tensing up, because that only made the pain worse. It would strike suddenly, without warning, but I knew this was only a temporary side effect and that eventually it would cease altogether. This took about six months, and it eased off gradually during that length of time.

I began to feel tired during the second week of treatment, and put this down to all the travelling. But the tiredness was another side effect of the radiotherapy, because this treatment can and does exhaust people, sometimes for a long while afterwards. I found I was very weary for over six months, but this was nothing in comparison to how the chemotherapy had made me feel.

The three weeks were soon over, and it felt fantastic driving home from Cambridge for the last time. Coming to the end of the radiotherapy was a really enormous milestone in our lives. The feeling we had at that point was beyond words. We said we couldn't have been happier if we'd won the lottery. As far as we were concerned, what we *had* won was my life and our future, the most precious and valuable things we could ever wish for. No amount of money could ever buy what we had been given.

That night we celebrated by opening a bottle of champagne a friend had brought me after my mastectomy "for medicinal purposes!" I'd been saving it especially for this momentous occasion. I don't believe anything could ever make us feel the way we did that night. It was one of the happiest times we have ever known.

My radiotherapy finished a couple of days before the Midsummer Solstice, the time of celebration of the peak of the Sun's position in the sky above. A time for acknowledging our energies and strengths, recognising all we have done during the past months to enable ourselves to reach our personal summits or goals. This was yet another amazing synchronicity. No time could have been more appropriate for us to celebrate the fact that both my chemotherapy and radiotherapy were over. At four a.m. on 21st June, Pete and I walked to a sheltered corner of a nearby field to wait for the sunrise. Together we watched our planet's life-giving star, in its dazzling, midsummer splendour, as it rose above the bank of low cloud hanging over the sea, a vivid, iridescent disc of luminosity, casting its light and warmth over the land as it ascended. We thought of the friends at Stonehenge whom we were with in spirit, and of all our people, gathered at ancient sacred sites across the world to witness this breathtaking spectacle. Some would have already seen it. Many were still awaiting it. Wherever we were, we stood in unity. For the two of us, the sun's rising on that longest day of the year was a moving sight and a profoundly sacred moment, for we felt its light touch us in more than just a physical way. The experience was deeply spiritual. It was as though we really were being shown that a bright future lay ahead for us. Each in our own way we offered thanks for our lives, and for the love we share, a love that enriches and enhances every day of our life together. Our hearts were overflowing with deep gratitude for the moment, the day, and for all the future midsummer risings of the sun, which we have never doubted we will live to see together, in the years yet to come.

Thirty-Nine

My treatment didn't end with the radiotherapy. The type of breast cancer I had often has to be treated with long-term medication, and the drug most commonly prescribed is called Tamoxifen. This is a hormone, and it is used to treat women whose breast cancer is oestrogen-dependent (oestrogen receptor positive). Tamoxifen blocks the oestrogen receptors in the body, so that cancer cells cannot lock onto the oestrogen that is in the receptors and grow into tumours, and its effectiveness in the prevention of secondary breast cancer is well established. It is taken as one daily tablet, usually for five years although sometimes people take it for longer or shorter periods of time.

Many women can tolerate this drug well enough to be able to take it for the prescribed period with few or no problems. But for a small minority (and it *is* a minority) the side effects can become too disabling to cope with, and I was one of these. I was still very badly affected by the menopausal symptoms of hot flashes and profuse sweating which had been induced by the chemotherapy, but the Tamoxifen made things very much worse and I was unable to take it for any longer than six months. The side effects kicked in only days after I'd begun taking it. I would wake at night feeling absolutely freezing, my flesh would be stone cold and I'd be shivering. The bedding used to become completely saturated with perspiration. I shook violently from head to foot, my teeth chattered, and I couldn't bear to move even an inch because the sheets were so wet and freezing cold that I couldn't bring myself to touch them. Pete kept one of his thermal tee shirts beside him in bed for me to put on at these times, and he used to help me get into them because I was so cold that I could hardly move. My body temperature dropped, and I didn't know what to do to deal with these appalling symptoms. We went back to sleeping in the same bed, so that Pete could help me get warm whenever I was struck with this intense cold after a hot sweat. He was very understanding and so good to me. He would rub my body all over to bring warmth back into it, and had very little sleep himself because of my problems. I would toss the duvet aside when I roasted, literally tearing off my nightie because I couldn't bear it on me; a few minutes later I'd scramble back into it and completely hog the duvet because I was so cold. We used to slip a couple of soft towels between me and the bottom sheet to help get me through the rest of the night, but each morning I'd have to completely strip the bed. During the daytime the same thing happened, sweat poured down my body in constant streams, drenching my clothes. I'd feel it running down my scalp, and my hair would be continuously soaked. It dripped from my forehead, and from my elbows. It trickled down my back, down the backs of my legs and into my socks. Sometimes my internal body heat became so intense that I thought I would spontaneously combust! Several times I fainted because these symptoms were just too much for my body to cope with.

After a couple of weeks of this torment I contacted my oncologist. She tried one or two different things over the next few months to see if these distressing symptoms could be alleviated. Medication is available that can relieve the sweats, as are various complementary therapies, and one of the drugs she prescribed, which I still take, stopped the night sweats completely. But none of the alternatives relieved the daytime heat and sweating. At first they worked for a week or two, but then I was back at square one. I wanted to discontinue taking the Tamoxifen, but the oncologist strongly advised against this, saying that I really needed to take it to prevent future recurrence of my breast cancer. I persevered for a while longer but in the end I just couldn't cope because my symptoms were intolerable. We had booked a trip to visit my sister in late summer, and I was really looking forward to seeing her. But we had to cancel this at the last minute because I was so ill.

Eventually the oncologist put me on an alternative breast cancer preventative drug, and I soon began to feel much better. The number of daily sweats diminished and life became bearable again. The flashes and sweats still trouble me, but not to the extent that they did before. Certain things will trigger a severe sweating reaction, such as emotional stress, hot food or drinks, warm environments and overly vigorous physical exercise. I have learned to pace myself, and I avoid situations and things that I know will bring on an attack, although sometimes one will happen for no apparent reason. But I only have four more years to wait before I am able to stop taking the preventative medication, and this thought spurs me on. It is still 'countdown time'.

Pete and I had really looked forward to the end of my radiotherapy, thinking life would be wonderful from then on, only to find I had to endure the distressing symptoms I have described, which even now will sometimes flare up and make my life difficult and uncomfortable. I find it tricky to buy clothes, because the only thing I can wear next to my skin now is pure cotton. Synthetic fabrics of all kinds are definitely out; I have only to be in an acrylic top for less than a minute before the sweat pours from my body. And as for wearing tights, forget it! During the winter when it was very cold, I preferred to freeze rather than wear woollen sweaters, because if I did my body heat used to become really intense and my clothes would be absolutely soaked with perspiration. When everybody else was in thick, warm clothes in the middle of January, I went shopping in a vest!

About fourteen months after the mastectomy I began to think I'd like to have my breast reconstructed. Pete wasn't happy about me having any more surgery. The mastectomy was my eighth operation and he thought I'd gone through enough in my life. But I got it into my head that he had been robbed, and this upset me more than anything. In all truthfulness, it was because of this that I thought about reconstruction; I didn't want it for me, and I never once grieved for the personal loss I had sustained. I wanted it for him, and I missed the softness against which I love to cuddle people and animals too. When I discussed my interest in reconstructive surgery with Pete he always told me he loved me just as I was, that I looked fine to him and to everyone else, and that he really thought I didn't need it. Despite his opinion I went to see a specialist in this field of breast surgery to find out what was entailed.

Pete came with me. I wanted him to be there so that he could hear what the surgeon had to say. She explained the procedures to us, telling us that because I'd had radiotherapy I wasn't a suitable candidate for tissue expansion and an implant. After radiotherapy the skin becomes very tight, losing its elasticity. The only method of reconstruction I was suitable for was what is called a 'Diep Flap'. In this method of reconstructive breast surgery, body tissues (skin, fat and blood vessels) are taken from the abdomen to the chest, to be moulded into a new breast. It is a marvellous method of reconstruction, and the results can be quite amazing. The 'breast' is lifelike, and being made of one's own body tissue it feels real to the touch. But it will not be as sensitive as was the original breast, being constructed primarily of just fat. A nipple has to be created separately. This is done some time after the initial reconstruction of the breast form, to allow the reconstructed breast to settle down and take its eventual shape and position. Some women prefer not to go this far and are happy to have the breast without the nipple. At the end of the day, whatever a woman wants she can have, and just about anything is possible.

The Diep Flap is a very complex procedure and the operation can take up to eight hours to perform. A scar on the tummy is inevitable, as is further scarring on the new breast. The surgeon told us that results are never guaranteed, and often a second or even third operation has to be carried out on the natural breast, to reshape it so that it will match the reconstructed one. She said I would be able to visit a few of her former patients before making my final decision, to see for myself some of the work she had done. But after hearing the details I decided I didn't want to proceed after all. Pete was clearly relieved. He'd already told me that the choice was mine, and that he would support any decision I made, but later he said he was glad I decided not to have the operation. The surgeon also supported my decision, saying it was as common for women to change their minds when they heard what was involved, as it was for them to want to proceed with the surgery. Every woman has the right to make her own choices, and after the consultation I was in no doubt that my decision not to have breast reconstruction was, for me, the right one. I was happy and content to remain just as I was, and all I wanted was to get on with my life, as before. I had only recently begun to feel that I was starting to recuperate after all the treatment I'd gone through, and didn't relish the thought of having to spend yet further months, possibly another year, recovering from surgery which, frankly, I knew I didn't really need.

I am thankful that I was able to make that decision with such conviction. I want to wear my 'medal', the mastectomy scar, proudly for the rest of my life. I cherish my relationship with the Amazons, because this taught me to think and fight like a warrior, and gave me the power over my enemy that enabled me to defy and defeat it. Now I have taken my place, to stand alongside countless thousands of other women as a fully qualified, lifelong member of the worldwide Amazon Sisterhood. I salute them all, trusting in my steadfast belief that I will be walking among them in the far distant future, as a battle-scarred, very old soldier.

Conclusion

My breast cancer happened to both of us. Although the disease attacked only one of our physical bodies, mentally and emotionally it struck both our hearts, both our minds and both our spirits. Pete and I each suffered it all; the shock of the diagnosis, the fear, the uncertainty and the treatment, and both of us were in need of healing. We helped ourselves to heal by understanding and accepting one another's pain. Instead of feeling sorry for ourselves we felt sorry for each other, and through our mutual sympathy we were able to understand exactly how the other person was thinking and feeling.

When people stopped us to ask how I was, or how the treatment was affecting me, I would politely remind them that Pete was there too, going through everything with me, asking them to remember this. This was only right, and only fair, because Pete was the one whose sole option at times was to look on helplessly as I struggled through my black days, and whenever things became too much for me he was there to see to whatever needed doing so that I could rest. I used to thank Pete every day (and still do) for all he did to make my life bearable, especially whilst I was having my chemotherapy treatment, always making certain he was aware of how much I appreciated his efforts, and that I recognised his personal contribution towards my recovery from breast cancer as being a most valuable and significant one. His response was always the same; he would tell me that he did what he did to help me because he loves me, and for no other reason. But I never took anything he did for granted, reminding myself at all times that however bad I was feeling, Pete was suffering with me. I often wonder if I would have been able to be as strong as he was if the situation had been reversed, and I'd been the one looking on, trying to remain cheerful and positive for his sake, knowing he was being treated for a potentially fatal disease, at times unable to do anything except just be there for him.

Mayday 2002 brought with it the first anniversary of the end of my chemotherapy, and we talked about our memories of that unforgettable day. I asked Pete how he felt about my cancer and the chemotherapy, now that we were one year on:

"It takes a long while to get it all out of your system. You don't lose it after a year; you don't lose it after two years. It's still there; you just put it to the back of your mind, into its little drawer. Every now and again the drawer will open and it will pop out at you. You have a quick look, then put it away again and close the drawer until next time."

Pete said he found things especially difficult when he was by himself, because then he thought about the serious side of the situation:

"When I was with you I saw you getting on with it, dealing with all the problems positively, always looking on the bright side, smiling and being so brave, even when you were having the chemotherapy. It wasn't until I really thought about what you were putting up with, until I stood back and considered the implications of what you were doing and why you were doing it, that I found it extremely difficult and upsetting. It just got harder as time went on."

Pete has always been mentally strong, able to deal with any crisis no matter how serious, and throughout our ordeal he never cracked. But now he says he finds it difficult, if not impossible, to be concerned with things that pale into insignificance and are trivial by comparison. His level of stress tolerance is nowhere near as high as it used to be. Things are by no means over for us yet, because I still have to pass the five-year survival threshold, although it is well over two years since I went for my first scans, and this is a positive sign. But for Pete, the stress of the uncertainty is more than enough to have to deal with. We cope with this together, just as we did when we were going through the 'cancer experience.' For the majority of the time we are very happy and content, but there are times when we need to talk about our anxieties and share our residual pain. As Pete rightly observed, these things don't go away for a very long time. Maybe they never will. I don't believe it is possible for anyone who has battled against cancer, or for their partner, to ever completely forget what it was like for them.

Pete cannot even think about the fact that I had breast cancer and a mastectomy without giving away some little sign that it still gets to him. It may be a tear in his eye, he may become quiet and thoughtful, or he may turn away and try to occupy himself with something, but that sign never fails to escape my notice. He often talks about the support of our friends, both at home and at his work. Without exception, every single one still makes enquiries to ask how I'm getting on or if I'm feeling okay, and this has helped to keep his spirits up more than anything. Pete always mentions it to me when someone has shown interest and concern, but never without those telltale, watery eyes that say far more. I have both read and heard it said that when someone has cancer, that person soon discovers who his or her real friends are. Pete and I echo this sentiment. It is because the thoughts of our friends are still with us that we know we are never alone, that someone is always there for us if ever we are in need.

As I write these words I look back and ask myself the questions "Have I really had breast cancer and survived to tell the tale? Did it really happen to me?" Even when I look at my scar I sometimes cannot believe it. There is also the issue of irrational 'survivor guilt' to consider, i.e. "What gives me the right to live when others may not be as fortunate?" This question has often proved too difficult for me to contemplate without feeling as if I'm being sucked into a deep mire of disturbed conscience, for there is no answer to it. All I can do is accept the fact that I *have* survived, and to do so with humility and infinite gratitude. But to be able to completely accept my fortuity is neither as easy nor as straightforward as might be imagined by someone who has never experienced cancer on a personal level, or seen the suffering.

Throughout my treatment I strove to maintain a positive mind-set, repeatedly telling myself "I *will* get better, I *am getting* better, I *am* better." This was helpful not only to me but also to Pete, for it enabled us both to still enjoy life, rather than allowing that natural fear which we all possess to take over and make life far more difficult than it needed to be. After my treatment was all over, Pete told me he would have found it much harder to cope with the situation we'd been in if I'd gone to pieces, because then he too would have been full of despair. He said he felt torn apart when he thought about me losing my breast, and more so when I was going through the chemotherapy, but that it was my strength that sustained him and enabled him to support me in the best ways he could. By facing my fear head-on, and challenging it, I was able to help us both. I refused to allow fear to dominate me by giving it the power to do so, just as I refused to dwell on the fact that I had breast cancer. Naturally the thought was often in my mind, but I learned to dismiss it almost as instantaneously as it arose, and to replace it with visualised images of myself as the fit and healthy woman I hoped to be in the fullness of time. My fight was a psychological one as well as a physical battle.

Throughout the entire experience of having breast cancer Pete's unfailing and loving support was my mainstay, and without him I know I would never have got through it as well as I did. Additionally, the fortitude and determination I needed to survive not only the shock of being told I had the disease, but also the subsequent surgery and treatment, was strengthened by my spiritual beliefs. In books of this nature, mention is often made of the writer's religious faith when this has played a major role in his or her recovery from serious illness or other catastrophe. My spiritual philosophy is based on the principle that Deity is to be found in all life, and in all of Nature's created things. I regard everything in the universe as being a manifestation of the Divine Source from which all life, love, goodness and healing flows. A couple of weeks after the start of my chemotherapy the month of October drew to its close, and with this came the time for celebrating what this period in the seasonal calendar means to me and to others with whom I share belief in the 'old wisdom'. It is the time for letting go, reflecting, recognizing what we have lost and gained during the past year, acknowledging how we have changed and evolved into what we have now become. With the arrival of the dark days of winter we release the old and look ahead to the new, letting go of everything that is no longer helpful or useful to us in our lives. It wasn't too difficult, therefore, to put my recent mastectomy behind me, after acknowledging it as a necessary step taken, from which I would continue to live, thrive and grow. The formidable presence of the threat the cancer posed to my future life was ritually banished. Consciously I welcomed the mastectomy scar as the sign of my triumph over this adversary, and allowed it to become as important and as meaningful a part of my body as was the breast it replaces. I spent the last, memorable night of that October in deep contemplation, feeling tangibly aware of my own changes, my losses, my gains, my new physical body, and was able to clearly see how the turmoil of the past two months had steered me gently but purposefully forward. Aided by the stabilising, inspirational, purifying and regenerative qualities of the elements, plus my own inner strength that has upheld me as I have progressed through my turbulent life, I have survived breast cancer and intend to continue to do so. Daily I give thanks for my many blessings, most especially for the love of my husband and for my recovery from the cancer. The answer to my prayer of gratitude may come in the rustle of the leaves of a tree as a sudden movement of breeze disturbs the stillness, or in the unexpected alighting of a bird upon the stump in the centre of the stone circle in our garden, or as a droplet of rain upon my brow. It may come as a sudden feeling of warmth on my face as the sun emerges unexpectedly from behind a cloud. Or in the flicker of a candle flame, casting its gentle glow around my room, its light reflected in the mirror on the wall behind it. I marvel at these things, consumed with awe at the magic of the inspiration they offer, glad that I can see their beauty, and that I am able to appreciate the value of their preciousness.

Every day I wake with a serene and contented state of mind, happy to be alive and full of gratitude for the life I have. The past is gone, and the future cannot even be imagined. Pete and I enjoy our life together to the full, focusing on the present. The dark, menacing clouds of cancer have no place in our radiant blue sky, and whatever the future may hold, the sun in all its glory will never cease to shine.

Postscript

Many of the early warning signs of breast cancer are symptomatic of other, benign conditions of the breast, and no woman should panic if she notices any of these changes because in many cases they are not indicative of cancer. But it is advisable for us all to be aware of what to look out for, to examine our breasts regularly even after menopause, and to continue to self-examine after having breast cancer. Ignorance is not bliss as far as this disease is concerned, and if we are fully informed regarding breast care and health we can look after ourselves properly. We owe it to our loved ones, and we owe it to ourselves, to be as breast aware as we possibly can. No woman should ever be too embarrassed to go to her doctor, or feel she is making a fuss, if she notices something unusual about her breast that alarms her. Any such change should be taken seriously and checked out as soon as possible.

Fear can and does cause some women to put off going to see their doctor because they are frightened that the lump they have found in their breast might be cancer. Once, I was talking to a woman who told me she'd had a breast lump for a while but was too scared to tell the doctor about it in case it turned out to be breast cancer. I persuaded her to have it looked at, and happily it turned out to be nothing serious. If more women were aware that *nine out of ten breast problems are not caused by cancer they might not feel so afraid of going to see a doctor as soon as an abnormality is discovered.

We all need to take charge of our own health and well being. The symptoms of breast cancer do not go away if they are ignored. It is our responsibility to take prompt action if we notice any change in our breasts at all, no matter how slight that change may be. If it worries you, get it looked at. Early diagnosis is a crucial factor in the successful treatment of breast cancer, and it is extremely important for any woman, or man, to get checked out straight away if they find anything unusual, especially a lump in their breast or a change in their

* Information from 'Breast Cancer Care' correct at time of writing

nipple. Men can and do develop breast cancer, and also have mastectomies. It is far more sensible for a man to have his own diagnosis of 'Jogger's Nipple' confirmed by a medical expert, than to ignore something that should be treated, and treated sooner rather than later.

As women get older the risk of developing breast cancer increases. Our national breast-screening programme offers mammography every three years to women between the ages of fifty and sixty-four. Ladies over this age are still able to go for screening even though they are not automatically invited to do so. Breast screening is available to the over sixty-fives on request.